NONCOOPERATIVE BREEDING IN THE CALIFORNIA SCRUB-JAY

William J. Carmen

Hastings Natural History Reservation and
Department of Forestry and Resource Conservation
University of California
Berkeley, California

Studies in Avian Biology No. 28
A PUBLICATION OF THE COOPER ORNITHOLOGICAL SOCIETY

Cover photograph of California Western Scrub-Jay (*Aphelocoma californica californica*) on California buckeye (*Aesculus californica*), Marin, California, by Ian Tait.

STUDIES IN AVIAN BIOLOGY

Edited by

John T. Rotenberry
Department of Biology
University of California
Riverside, CA 92521

This volume is dedicated to Frank A. Pitelka (1916–2003),
Editor of STUDIES IN AVIAN BIOLOGY from 1984 to 1987.

Studies in Avian Biology is a series of works too long for *The Condor*, published at irregular intervals by the Cooper Ornithological Society. Manuscripts for consideration should be submitted to the editor. Style and format should follow those of previous issues.

Price $15.00 including postage and handling. All orders cash in advance; make checks payable to Cooper Ornithological Society. Send orders to Cooper Ornithological Society, *c/o* Western Foundation of Vertebrate Zoology, 439 Calle San Pablo, Camarillo, CA 93010.

ISBN: 0-943610-59-1

Library of Congress Catalog Number: 2004105550
Printed at Cadmus Professional Communications, Ephrata, PA 17522
Issued: 15 October 2004

CONTENTS

TABLES

FIGURES

Studies in Avian Biology No. 28:1–100, 2004

ABSTRACT

I studied the ecology, behavior, and demography of the noncooperatively breeding Western Scrub-Jay (*Aphelocoma californica californica*) in central coastal California. Cooperative breeding is ancestral in *Aphelocoma* jays and its loss in Western Scrub-Jays presents an opportunity for appropriate phylogenetic and ecological comparisons within the genus to identify key factors selecting for the alternative social systems. My intent was to gather comparative data to test several models for the evolution and maintenance of delayed dispersal and group living in birds, which were developed from long-term studies of cooperative breeders, including the closely related Florida Scrub-Jay (*A. coerulescens*) and Mexican Jay (*A. ultramarina*). The fundamental result of these comparisons is that models for the evolution of delayed dispersal and group living in birds fail as general explanations when floating is ignored or treated as a one-dimensional phenomenon. Factors that lead to delayed dispersal in cooperative species are known to be complex and may differ substantially among species and populations, and even among individuals within populations and groups. Conditions leading to early dispersal and floating may be equally complex. Clearly, opportunities for independent breeding are constrained in both cooperative and noncooperative populations. What then makes early dispersal and floating the preferred strategy in Western Scrub-Jays? Several factors play a part, including (1) the interplay between the pattern of habitat quality and acorn production, (2) the varied behaviors floaters may employ to exploit these resources and acquire breeding space, (3) the behavioral interactions between territorial jays and floaters, and (4) the ability of floaters to settle on low-quality territories and then, as breeders, to move and improve the quality of their territories.

California Scrub-Jays are monogamous, permanently territorial, and noncooperative breeders. Offspring depart from their natal territories at independence, yet breeders tolerate both offspring and unrelated floaters of all ages on their territories except during May and June. Because of this tolerance, juveniles and older floaters aggregate in the highest quality habitats on occupied territories, primarily where acorns are in good supply. Although floaters exhibit diverse dispersal behavior, most remain sedentary throughout the winter and early spring, storing and recovering acorns as do the resident territorial breeders. By late April in most years, the aggregations dissolve and floaters are rarely seen until some of these same individuals return in early July and join large numbers of independent juveniles. The disappearance of floaters is coincidental with increased aggression by territorial jays, but floaters also disappear from areas not occupied by breeders.

Floating in scrub-jays took several forms. Some banded juveniles remained on and around their natal territories until the next breeding season, others joined aggregations a short distance away or disappeared. In four of five years, the study area attracted floaters from a wide area. In the anomalous year (when the acorn crop failed), local juveniles departed and no floaters immigrated. In winter, floaters occasionally established pseudo-territories that were abandoned in the late spring. Other floaters moved widely (up to 35 km) during the winter, but the majority established defined home-ranges from fall to early spring. In April of one year, large flocks of up to 60 jays in transit were observed. The few floaters seen during May and June in most years were individually sneaking through territories or, more rarely, moving in unoccupied habitat. In one year (1985) of high acorn abundance lasting until April, floaters remained on their home ranges (which overlapped an average of nine territories) throughout the breeding season; this was coupled with increased tolerance by breeders.

Breeder survivorship averaged 83% and 79% per year for males and females, respectively, and reproductive output averaged 1.4 fledglings per pair. Reproductive success of jays that acquired territories as yearlings was near zero and did not peak until age four.

Over the five-year period and 215 pair-years, first-year males and females comprised 5% and 10%, respectively, of the breeding population. Of 12 jays that both fledged from and later acquired territories on the study area, five did so as yearlings, four as two-year olds, and three as three-year olds. Nearly all jays gained a territory by pairing with an older, established breeder. Life-table estimates, based upon these and other demographic data, indicate that 19% and 40% of males and females, respectively, acquire territories as yearlings. An analysis of territorial dynamics, including the types of habitats used, occupancy rates of territories, and vegetation characteristics, suggest that all suitable habitat is occupied by breeders in most years and that ecological constraints prevent a sizeable portion of first-year jays from acquiring territories and breeding.

Individual jays cache approximately 7,000 acorns each year. Poor acorn years result in significantly higher mortality, reproductive failure, and territory abandonment. The 1983 crop failure, through the effects of higher mortality and territory abandonment, resulted in a 25% decrease in the number of territories on the study area and the potential for new breeding vacancies. Acorn production by the large and patchily distributed oaks in California is highly variable locally within and among years, and periodic crop failures occur every 4 to 6 years, depending on the number of oaks species in the area.

Early dispersal is favored because floaters are able to aggregate in areas of high acorn abundance, and the tolerance of floaters by breeders allows them access to the best habitats. Floaters appear to be as dependent on cached acorns as breeders and may be closely tied to these stores during the winter. Floaters may spend fall and winter in areas of high acorn production, despite the fact that these areas provide relatively few breeding opportunities. In the spring, near continuous distribution of oak woodland provides lepidopteran larvae and other insects over a wide area. Floaters are then free to move regionally and search out breeding areas, particularly in areas of prior acorn crop failures that may offer more territory vacancies. This pattern of food abundance may also contribute to the tolerance of floaters in the winter (when acorns are superabundant) and intolerance in the breeding season (when insect prey is important and starvation rates of nestlings are high).

Key words: *Aphelocoma*, acorn production, cooperative breeding, dispersal, floating, scrub-jay, social behavior.

INTRODUCTION

Long-term field studies have contributed greatly to our knowledge of the demographic and ecological factors that promote delayed dispersal, larger group size, and increased cooperation in cooperatively breeding birds. Theories based on these studies differ in stressing the relative importance of various demographic and ecological factors both in the maintenance of cooperative breeding and in modeling the evolution of group living and cooperative breeding from an earlier noncooperative state. Similar long-term studies of appropriate noncooperative species are essential for the comparisons required to test these theories and their underlying assumptions. The Western Scrub-Jay (*Aphelocoma californica*) and other species in the genus provide a unique and unparalleled opportunity to make such comparisons. *Aphelocoma* jays are similar in morphology and general aspects of behavior, their social organization ranges from the noncooperative Western Scrub-Jay to the plural-breeding, cooperative Mexican Jay (*A. ultramarina*), and there is a wealth of information on two cooperative members of the genus, the Mexican Jay and the Florida Scrub-Jay (*A. coerulescens*).

APHELOCOMA JAYS

Nearly all races of scrub-jays in western North America breed noncooperatively. Young disperse from their natal territories soon after becoming independent and then, over the ensuing months, attempt to acquire territories and breeding status. Despite their wide geographic range and the diversity of habitats used, only one population (*A. californica sumichrasti*) in the mountains of southeastern Mexico is known to live in family groups (Burt and Peterson 1993).

The insular Island Scrub-Jay (*Aphelocoma insularis*) has been the best studied western population (Atwood 1980a,b; Atwood et al. 1990); it became isolated from the mainland population during the Pleistocene (Pitelka 1951), almost certainly after the western populations had lost traits of cooperative breeding (see below). In contrast to the noncooperative Western Scrub-Jays, the cooperatively breeding Florida Scrub-Jay (Woolfenden 1974, 1975; Woolfenden and Fitzpatrick 1977, 1978, 1984, 1986, 1990; Fitzpatrick and Woolfenden 1986, 1988; Mumme 1992) and Mexican Jay (Brown 1963, 1970, 1974, 1994; Brown and Brown 1981a, 1984, 1990; Brown et al. 1997; Trail et al. 1981) have been intensively studied for 25+ years. In Florida Scrub-Jays, offspring from a single breeding pair may delay dispersal for one to several years, forego breeding, and help in defending the territory and raising offspring in subsequent breeding efforts. Roughly one-half of all pairs have helpers in any given year. The Mexican Jay exhibits geographic variation in group size and social behavior (Strahl and Brown 1987, Brown and Horvath 1989) ranging from singular breeding (one breeding female per group) to up to five breeding pairs on a single group territory. Offspring may delay dispersal and breeding for up to six years and help; some offspring never disperse but become breeders on their natal territories. Both nonbreeders and breeders participate in territory defense and care for young at all group nests. Less is known of the Unicolored Jay (*Aphelocoma unicolor*), but it does breed cooperatively and exhibits behavioral characteristics intermediate between those of Florida Scrub-Jays and Mexican Jays: intermediate group sizes, a single female breeder, and possibly more than one breeding male per group (Pitelka 1951, Webber and Brown 1994).

The occurrence of cooperative breeding in the Florida Scrub-Jay, Mexican and Unicolor jays, in one population of Western Scrub-Jay (*A. californica sumichrasti*), and in some or all species studied in closely related genera (*Cyanolyca*, *Cyanocorax*, *Cissilopha*, and *Calocitta*; reviewed in Brown 1987), suggests that cooperative behavior is a primitive character state shared with other Middle and South American jays (Edwards and Naeem 1993). Indeed, even other more distantly related corvids exhibit varying aspects of group living and cooperative breeding (e.g., Gray Jays, *Perisoreus canadensis* [Waite and Strickland 1997]; western American Crows, *Corvus brachyrhynchos hesperis* [Caffrey 1992]), and a wide variety of other avian taxa show at least facultative or incidental helping behaviors (see Brown 1987). If group living and cooperative breeding are ancestral and Western Scrub-Jays have lost the behavior (Pitelka 1986, Peterson and Burt 1992; but see Brown and Li 1995), why then are California Scrub-Jays so adamantly noncooperative?

OVERVIEW

Proposed hypotheses and models have invoked a variety of ecological, demographic, and behavioral processes as key factors in the evolution and maintenance of group living and cooperative breeding. Most theories for the evolution of group living and cooperative breeding postulate that social groups form because individuals lack opportunities to disperse and breed successfully themselves. Such opportunities may be limited by a shortage of mates (Rowley 1965, Pruett-Jones and Lewis 1990); by the ability of groups, but not pairs, to breed successfully (Rabenold 1984, 1985; Austad and Rabenold 1985, 1987); and by a high variance in resource levels and carrying capacity, leading to either a high cost of independent breeding (Emlen 1982), to closures of intermittently open breeding vacancies (Brown 1987), or a general lack of suitable breeding territories (Selander 1964; Brown 1974, 1978). Other theories stress the importance of the distribution of habitat quality (Koenig and Pitelka 1981) or the variance in territory quality (Stacey and Ligon 1987, 1991) in selecting for delayed dispersal and group living. Others point out that where resource renewal is slow, group size may be limited to pairs, despite other factors favoring retention of offspring (Waser 1981, Brown 1982). Finally, virtually every study of cooperative breeders suggests significant direct or indirect inclusive fitness benefits, or both, accruing to individuals that delay dispersal and assist their parents or siblings in some manner. Although California Scrub-Jays do not delay dispersal and help, ancestral populations almost certainly did so, and the loss of the fitness benefits associated with group living and cooperative breeding must be taken into account.

Examining the importance of these factors requires data on food resources and foraging, territorial behavior and territory quality, dispersal, reproduction, and survivorship. Such information for the California Scrub-Jay is presented in the central sections of this monograph. An essential part of the comparisons among populations must focus on nonbreeders: helpers in cooperative species, floaters in noncooperative ones. Acquiring data on nonbreeding floaters is notoriously difficult, and floaters have most often been ignored or written-off as "surplus population." Floaters are, of course, as integral to a population as nonbreeding helpers, and are a primary focus of this monograph.

The penultimate section of this volume uses these data to draw comparisons among *Aphelocoma* jays and to test the predictions of the various models and hypotheses. It should be noted that these models approach the evolution of group living and cooperative breeding as proceeding from an earlier noncooperative state. Here, the transition is from an ancestral cooperative state to a noncooperative one, and there is no a priori reason to suspect that evolutionary factors are symmetrical in their effects. This may also complicate comparisons among populations in that certain behaviors may be relics of an ancestral cooperative social system.

In the final section, I show how specific factors affect Western Scrub-Jays in California —from the pattern of acorn production to the suite of strategies available to floaters for gaining a territory—and contribute to the loss of cooperative breeding while favoring early dispersal and floating.

STUDY AREA AND METHODS

LOCATION OF STUDY AREA

The 900-ha Hastings Natural History Reservation lies in the outer coast range of central California at the upper end of the Carmel Valley, 36 km from the Pacific Ocean. To the southwest the Santa Lucia Range rises to 1,538 m on Chews Ridge, and to the east Palo Escrito Peak tops the Sierra de Salinas at 1,362 m (Fig. 1).

I studied scrub-jays primarily on Big Creek, in the lower portion of the Reservation.

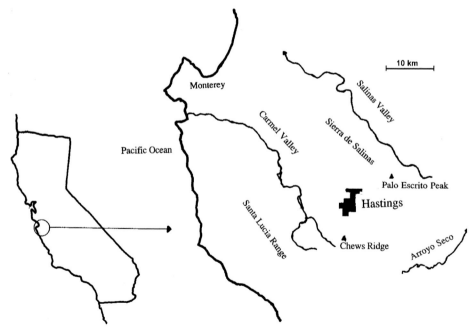

FIGURE 1. Location of the Hastings Reservation in relation to local geographic and topographic landmarks.

Big Creek flows through the center of the site, and four hills (470–637 m) rise nearby (Fig. 2). In 1981, the first year of the study, the study area covered 83 ha, and in 1982 through 1985, 197 ha. Within the study area all major vegetation and habitat types found in the surrounding area are represented. Other parts of the Reservation, and neighboring ranches, were surveyed occasionally for floaters and to monitor dispersal.

CLIMATE

The Reservation has a Mediterranean climate; the summers are dry and warm, and the winters wet and cold. Almost no rain falls between May and October, and late summer and early fall are extremely hot and dry. Rainfall over the last 40 years has averaged 52 cm. Mean monthly temperature and precipitation are roughly inversely related. July is the hottest and driest month; the wettest months are December through March. Figure 3 presents 40-year averages for temperature and precipitation at the Reservation headquarters, at the center of the study area. The creeks stop flowing in late summer in most years; Finch and Robertson creeks always hold some pools through the summer whereas Big Creek dries up completely. Snow falls on the higher elevations of the Reservation several times in most winters, but rarely persists for more than a day.

VEGETATION

Vegetation is predominantly oak woodland and is similar to foothill vegetation found throughout the central coast ranges. Six important plant communities, as defined in

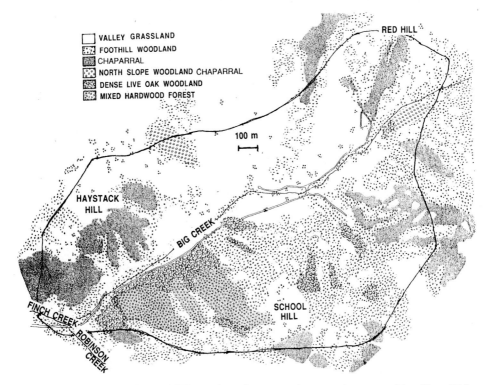

FIGURE 2. Study area showing local hills, creeks, and representative vegetation communities. The solid line encloses the study area of 1982–1985 (197 hectares).

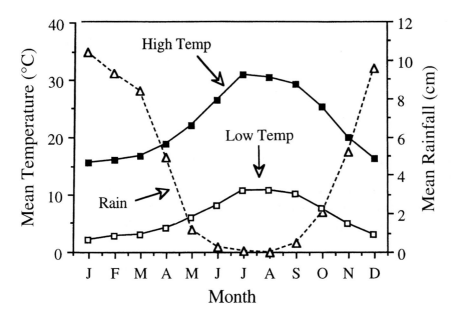

FIGURE 3. Forty-year mean rainfall and mean maximum and minimum temperatures at the Hastings Reservation (1938–1978).

Barbour and Major (1977), are found on the scrub-jay study area:
1) Mixed hardwood forest (*Quercus agrifolia-Arbutus*).
2) Foothill woodland (*Q. lobata-Q. douglasii*).
3) North slope woodland-chaparral (*Aesculus californica-Q. agrifolia* phase).
4) Chaparral (*Adenostoma fasciculatum-Ceanothus cuneatus*).
5) Riparian forest (*Salix-Platanus* phase).
6) Valley grassland (*Bromus-Avena-Erodium*).

The distribution of these communities on the study area (except for the riparian communities) is mapped in Figure 2. By far the most dominant trees, and most important to the scrub-jays, are the oaks. On the Reservation there are six species representing all three oak subgenera. On the study area, three of these species are common (*Q. agrifolia*, *Q. lobata*, and *Q. douglasii*) whereas *Q. kelloggii* is rare and *Q. chrysolepis* and *Q. wizlizenii* are absent; however, *Q. kelloggii* and *Q. chrysolepis* are abundant within 1 km.

METHODS

Banding

Between July 1977 and March 1981, prior to the start of this study, 43 jays were banded, either with color bands or with U.S. Fish and Wildlife Service (USFWS) bands only. Eleven of these jays were found as breeders on the study area in April 1981 at the start of the study. Beginning in 1981, my field assistants and I banded 779 scrub-jays: 106 as breeders, 350 as nestlings, and 323 as nonbreeding floaters. I use the terms "breeder" and "territorial jay" interchangeably; floaters are nonterritorial and nonbreeding individuals. Jays were given unique band combinations consisting of three plastic colored bands (8 colors) and a USFWS aluminum band. The plastic wrap-around color bands were sealed with acetone.

I captured breeders and floaters almost exclusively with ground traps baited with acorns, but a small percentage was captured with mist nets at water sources in July through September. Nestlings were banded at 10 days of age.

Age determination

When first caught, scrub-jays were aged according to molt and feather wear (Pitelka 1945). I use the following terminology to describe age classes:

1) juveniles (up to five months old): individuals between fledging and near conclusion of post-juvenile molt (approximately 1 October). Juveniles have gray heads and other less obvious plumage characteristics that separate them easily from other age classes.

2) first-year birds (up to 12 months old): individuals from fledging through the next spring (31 May). Thus I refer to jays breeding in the spring following hatching as first-year birds. In the post-juvenile molt, jays molt their body feathers, but most flight feathers (and coverts) are retained (Pitelka 1945). This allows first-year jays to be distinguished from adults easily in the hand and, with practice, in the wild.

3) adults (+12 months old): all individuals after the first spring (1 June) following hatching. Between June and September three age classes could be identified: juveniles (young of the year), second-year jays (hatched the previous spring, entering their second year and undergoing their first complete molt), and jays entering their third year or older.

Sex determination

All breeders were sexed by behavioral criteria; only females incubate, brood young, and give the sex-specific "rattle call." Females are also slightly smaller, duller in plumage, and weigh less than their mates. Side by side, the sexes of a known pair are usually easily recognized.

Floaters could not be sexed in the field unless a female gave a rattle call, or a male engaged in courtship feeding with a known female floater. To ascertain the sex of floaters I performed discriminant function analyses, based upon weight and wing-cord measurements on breeders and floaters from the study area, all of known sex. The single discriminant function (N = 150, χ^2 = 133.9, df = 2, P <0.001) correctly classified 89% of 79 females and 89% of 71 males. An independent data set was taken from museum specimens (University of California Museum of Vertebrate Zoology) collected on or near the Hastings Reservation. These 36 females and 25 males included only adults and first-year birds. The discriminant function derived from the first sample correctly classified 93.4% of the independent data set (94.4% of females and 92% of males) and was then used to sex the floaters captured on the study area.

Nest checks

I attempted to find every nest each year as early as possible in the breeding season. Beginning in late February, I began monitoring the banded breeders and tried to locate nests during nest building, when the task is easiest. After egg laying, the jays become secretive and locating nests often took hours or several days. Locating nests was difficult because jays may nest from 0.5 to 15 m above the ground in shrubs, lichens, mistletoe, old magpie nests, and in oak canopies. My attempts to entice nest-building females with nesting material in order to follow them back to the nest, as is sometimes possible with Florida Scrub-Jays (G. Woolfenden, pers. comm.), proved unsuccessful.

Nearly all nests were found before or soon after egg laying. A few nests were lost to predators before they were located, but even in those cases I knew, from the pair's be-havior, whether the pair had a nest with eggs. For example, prior to egg-laying the pair would be vocal and easily observed; after egg-laying the female would rarely be seen, and the male would be comparatively unobtrusive and would collect food to feed to the female. I failed to locate only one nest that successfully fledged young (out of 215 pair-years and a total of 315 nests).

Once located, nest checks were kept at a minimum. I visited only to determine first egg date (FED), clutch size, and hatching brood size, and to band the nestlings. The jays vociferously defend their nests and thus may attract any of a suite of predators. My activi-ties, primarily in 1981, led to the loss of nests by attracting other scrub-jays, American Crows, Yellow-billed Magpies (*Pica nuttalli*), and Cooper's Hawks (*Accipter cooperii*). To minimize the impacts of my activities, nests were checked with a mirror attached to a 1-m staff, and in many cases I did not need to approach the nest closely until banding. Nests that were difficult to reach were checked only at the estimated hatching date and at banding, or just at banding to minimize the chance of attracting predators. This resulted in some loss of data, but minimized bias due to human interference; in cases where I thought my activities caused nest or nestling loss, I excluded the record from all analyses.

Nests were visited on the estimated day of fledging to count the number fledging, and then one month and two months later to count the number of independent young. Although young may be fed up to three months after fledging, they usually disperse from their natal territories 7 to 8 weeks after fledging. Between nest checks, pairs and nests were watched to confirm whether the nests were still active. If not, the nest was examined to determine cause of loss, and the new nest (if any) subsequently located. Local scrub-jays fledge only one brood per year but will renest up to three times if earlier nests fail.

Territory mapping

Beginning in March of each year, locations of the banded breeders were recorded on aerial photographs (1 cm = 12.5 m) of the study area. In addition, defended boundar-ies were marked where disputes occurred. By August, the accumulated locations and defended boundary locations were used to delineate territories. Although I mapped ter-ritories only during the breeding season, pairs defended their territories throughout the year. Changes in boundaries may occur at any time, usually as a result of breeder death; such changes and their presumed cause were noted. Throughout this volume specific ter-ritory names are indicated in capitals, e.g. BURNT, 2400R, NTN, and can be located on the territory maps.

Operationally, I use both defended area (Noble 1939) and exclusive use (Pitelka 1959) to define the territory boundaries. In some cases, especially where territories were not apparently contiguous, I used a tape recorder to play vocalizations to attract breeders and locate borders. Territory size was measured by tracing boundaries with a digital planim-eter; no compensation was made for differences in slope.

Vegetation sampling

Two methods were used to sample vegetation characteristics. First, vegetation throughout the Reservation was measured (W. Koenig, unpubl. data) employing the methods of James and Shugart (1970). On 0.04 ha plots (N = 246) placed every 60 m on a grid, the following were recorded: (1) the species and diameter at breast height (DBH) of all trees; (2) estimates of percent coverage of tree canopy, shrubs, and grass; and (3) the species of trees observed within the 60 m grid unit but not within the 0.04 ha plot. Each sample covered approximately 10% of the total area of a grid unit.

Second, on aerial photographs of the study area, I used a digital planimeter to measure the following on 24 territories: (1) total area; (2) area of canopy cover of oaks; (3) area of canopy of other trees; (4) area of chaparral; (5) area of other brush; and (6) area of open grassland. These data were used to relate vegetation characteristics to occupied and unoccupied habitats and to the overall quality of territories.

Breeder censuses

The study population of banded breeders was censused periodically to acquire data on survivorship and breeder movements. Censuses occurred in early October, early January, early April, and early July, and pairs were monitored on a weekly basis from mid-March to mid-July in conjunction with nest checks. Each complete census took 10–14 days.

Floater censuses

During 1981–1982 and 1982–1983, monthly surveys were conducted on all territories and unoccupied areas on the study area. In each location the number of floaters (nonterritorial jays) was estimated. Floaters, especially during the nonbreeding season, tended to aggregate and to be vocal, bold, and easily observed. Many were banded, and I remained on an area until most sightings were repeats. In areas with no apparent floaters, I remained at least 1 h, during which I played vocalizations from a tape recorder to attract any jays in the area.

Floater sightings

In the course of the study, floaters were identified by their color bands, and their location was noted. Over 2,196 resightings of 276 color-banded floaters (including jays born on the study area and immigrants) were recorded. These data were used to examine juvenile dispersal, floater associations, floater movements, and the transition from floater to breeder status.

Behavioral observations

Between August 1981 and March 1984, I collected time-activity budgets on territorial breeders. Focal-animal sampling (Altmann 1974) on each individual lasted for 1 to 4 h (mean of 3 h). A composite day for each individual was completed over a one- or two-day period. I made a continuous record of all behaviors, with transitions between behaviors recorded to the nearest 10 s. Each hour was considered an individual sample period, and percentage of time in different activities was calculated as a percentage of time the jay was in view. Particular attention was focused on foraging behavior and method (e.g., leaf gleaning, hawking, caching acorns, recovering acorns), and territorial behavior (e.g., breeder-breeder and breeder-floater interactions). Data were collected every month (mean of 35 h per month) between July 1981 and March 1984, except for January through March and October through November 1983. Because I was able to follow individual floaters for only short periods, I quantified foraging behavior by recording the second foraging movement after initial contact on each individual. This was also done for breeders so that breeder and floater foraging behavior could be compared directly.

Radio-tracking

Floaters were radio-tracked to acquire data on juvenile dispersal, home-range movements, and habitat use. Radio backpacks were glued to the backs of jays and further secured with a harness (5 g total weight). Radio batteries lasted from 4 to 10 weeks. Radios were placed on 16 birds: (1) three juveniles five weeks post-fledging, just prior to dispersal in 1984; (2) two first-year floaters during the winter, 1984–1985; and (3) 11 floaters during the breeding season in 1985 (one adult, 10 first-year jays). Jays were followed for 3-h periods, and locations marked on aerial photographs every 10 min. From observations over one- or two-day periods, composite days were compiled from morning, midday, and evening watches. During the watches, in addition to locations, data were collected on interactions with breeders, other floaters, and foraging behavior. The tagged jays became accustomed to observers and could usually be kept in sight. In all, 618 h of radio-tracking data were collected on tagged jays. I also performed 27 "simultaneous" locations on all of the tagged jays during the breeding season in 1985 to detect grouping.

Food assessment

Scrub-jays eat a wide variety of foods, which makes sampling resources difficult. I settled on several methods to estimate the relative abundance of two important foods: insects during the breeding season, and acorns in the fall. The relative abundance of flying insects was measured with a series of 9 yellow pan traps filled with water and surface tension broken with a drop of liquid dish soap (Southwood 1978). The yellow pans were emptied weekly, and the collected insects classified to order, dried, and weighed (W. Koenig, unpubl. data). Data on relative abundance of ground and grass dwelling insects were provided by P. Williams, who performed weekly sweep-net samples during the breeding season. These samples consisted of 100 sweeps of a butterfly net across an open field (valley grassland community) at the center of the study area. Collected insects were dried and weighed. I attempted to estimate the relative abundance of lepidopteran larvae, the major food of young nestlings (Verbeek 1970; pers. obs.) by examining 1,000 oak leaves weekly (Perrins 1976). Even when the jays were gleaning large numbers of larvae, the only kind I counted in sufficient numbers were those of the California oak moth (*Phryganidia californica*), which is not eaten by jays. The relative abundance of acorns was visually estimated each fall (Carmen et al. 1987, Koenig et al. 1994a). We sampled 250 oaks of five common species. On each tree, two observers counted as many acorns as possible in 15 s and the two counts were combined for "acorns per 30 s." Each tree was also scored on a scale from 0 (no acorns) to 4 (a bumper crop). In addition, four traps were placed under each of two trees of each species to determine the temporal pattern of acorn fall.

FOOD AND FORAGING

Food abundance and foraging behavior have fundamental influences on the social behavior of birds. Verbeek (1970) and Brown (1974) hypothesized that the differences in social behavior in jays and other corvids were primarily the result of the various exploitation patterns resulting from patterns of food abundance and foraging behavior. A distinct and important behavior that all jays share is food caching; numerous species of birds, including *Aphelocoma* jays, cache food (Smith and Reichman 1984, Vander Wall 1990), primarily seeds, and studies have shown that differences in annual seed abundance affect the timing of reproduction, reproductive success, and behavior of seed caching birds (Perrins 1970, Vander Wall and Balda 1977, van Balen 1980, Koenig and Mumme 1987). In this section, I examine how food abundance and foraging behaviors of scrub-jays varied seasonally and annually, and how this variation affected their social behavior.

SEASONAL ABUNDANCE OF FOOD

Many studies at Hastings have measured food resources thought to be important to several avian species. These data give a broad picture of average seasonal variation in scrub-jays' food availability. Early in the breeding season, jays forage predominantly by leaf-gleaning when oak-leaf arthropods are available, especially on live oaks (*Q. agrifolia*; Fig. 4a). Grasshoppers are important later in spring and early summer, and their abundance shows an abrupt rise in May and decline in July in most years (Fig. 4b). During this study, other research workers and I quantified the relative abundance of ground-dwelling invertebrates (P. Williams, unpubl. data; Fig. 4c) and flying insects (W. Koenig, unpubl. data; Fig. 4d). These data indicate that invertebrate abundance is typically low in March through mid-April, increases sharply in late April, and peaks in May and early June. By August, with the onset of the late summer dry period, all samples of invertebrate abundance decrease.

Although seasonal buildup and total relative abundance of invertebrates differed among years, variation in acorn abundance was even greater. In a 12-year study of acorn production patterns at the Hastings Reservation, the oak species tended to produce acorns asynchronously, with crop failures occurring every 4 to 7 years; the probability of an poor acorn crop was directly related to the number of oak species in the area (Carmen et al. 1987, Koenig et al. 1994b). Between 1971 and 1987 three crops failed; two (1973 and 1983) were localized and affected lower elevations of the Reservation (MacRoberts and MacRoberts 1976, Carmen et al. 1987), one in 1978 was extensive (Koenig and Mumme 1987). Over the study period, acorn production was good in four years and poor in one (1983, Fig. 5). In the poor year, however, acorns were abundant within 3 km of the study area.

Another important factor in acorn availability is the length of time acorns are retained on the trees, being greatest in *Q. agrifolia* (Fig. 6). Once acorns fall they are rapidly lost to acorn consumers; in contrast, those on the tree are available to just a few seed eaters, and therefore represent a valuable and long lasting food resource for jays, both for immediate consumption and for caching.

SEASONAL FORAGING BEHAVIOR OF BREEDERS AND FLOATERS

Foraging of breeders

A total of 2,456 foraging observations on territorial jays (minimum of 100 observations in any month) were recorded between July 1981 and December 1982, years with good acorn crops. Foraging activity was expressed as a proportion of all observations, with observations from the same month in different years pooled (Fig. 7). Beginning in August and continuing through February, acorns eaten directly off the tree or from the ground ranged from 16% of all recorded foraging events in February to 31% in October. Jays began storing acorns and, to a lesser degree insects, worms, and other foods, in large numbers in September (25% of all foraging activity), and continued to do so into March

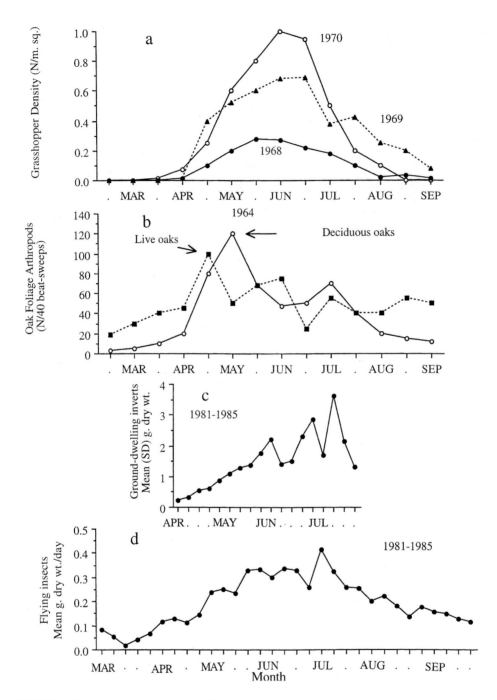

FIGURE 4. Relative abundance and seasonality of invertebrates at the Hastings Reservation: a) grasshopper density 1968–1970 (Verbeek 1970); b) oak-foliage arthropods from beat-sweep samples in 1964 (Root 1967); c) ground-dwelling invertebrates from sweep-net samples 1981–1985 (P. Williams, unpubl. data); and d) flying invertebrates from yellow-pan catch traps, 1981–1985 (W. Koenig, unpubl. data).

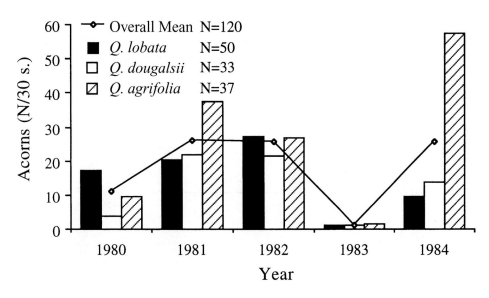

FIGURE 5. Relative abundance (30-s counts) of acorns produced by the three common species of oaks on the scrub-jay study area from 1980–1984. The line indicates overall mean for the three oak species.

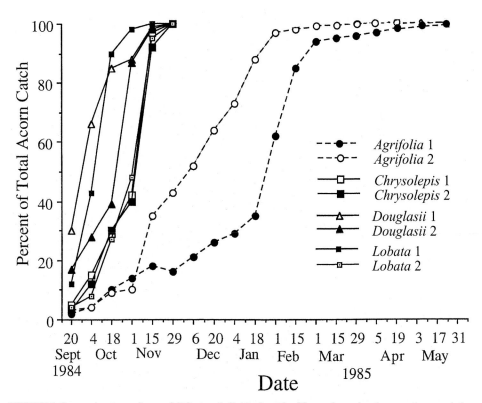

FIGURE 6. Seasonal pattern of acorn fall for two individuals each of four oak species shown as the cumulative percentage of total fall. Data are from acorns collected in acorn traps on a weekly basis, with four traps under two trees of each species.

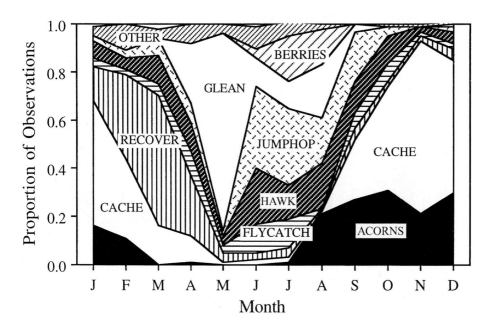

FIGURE 7. Seasonal change in foraging activities of territorial jays over the year expressed as a proportion of all foraging activity (see text for explanation).

(16%). Jays scatterhoarded intact acorns in the ground on their territories; perishable foods (e.g., partially eaten acorns, insects, earthworms, parts of animals) were cached off the ground in lichens and bark. The vast majority of food stored (>90%) was acorns, but jays might store any temporarily abundant food, such as swarming ants and bees. Jays did not recover much stored food until January (14% of foraging activities), but in February and March recovering stored food comprised the better part of foraging effort (Fig. 7). Acorns made up the vast majority of food items recovered during this period.

In April, jays shifted to invertebrate foods, primarily by gleaning lepidopteran larvae from oak leaves; by mid-April and May this constituted 79% of all foraging events, suggesting that such larvae are abundant earlier than other invertebrate foods (see Fig. 4). Lepidopteran larvae, which have a relatively high protein content compared to plant material, constitute approximately 60% of the nestling diet (Verbeek 1970). Jays recovered cached acorns even in May and fed acorns to their older nestlings (Verbeek 1970; pers. obs.). Acorns contain mostly carbohydrates and moderate amounts of lipids (Wainio and Forbes 1941, Ofcarcik and Burns 1971), but high tannin levels (Ofcarcik and Burns 1971), and their detrimental effects on growth rate (Marquardt and Ward 1979) and bone development (Elkin et al. 1978) may make them unsuitable for younger nestlings.

By June and through July, jays used several different foraging methods, such as hawking (flying from low perches to capture insects on the ground), jump-hopping (hopping through the grass and leaf-litter, scaring up insects), and flycatching (aerial sallies), reflecting the wider array of foods available to them.

Acorn use, foraging behavior, and time budgets

I studied time-budgets of territorial jays from August 1981 through February 1984. This period included two years of good acorn production (1981 and 1982) and one (1983) of local failure. Time budgets from April through July were similar in all years, and breeders spent an average of 71% of all daylight hours foraging (Fig. 8). This sample excludes incubating and brooding females as well as breeders without eggs or nestlings. The high percentage of foraging time, therefore, reflects the high demands of the male foraging for himself and his incubating mate, and both adults foraging for young. In good years, jays reduced their foraging time beginning in August, when acorns became available and began to make up a large part of the diet, and from August through March spent only 36% of the day foraging. In contrast, during the poor acorn year, jays foraged significantly longer, averaging 64% of daylight hours in August and December through February (Fig. 8).

In good years, jays spent an average of 70% of their foraging time (or 25% of total time) from October through March looking for, eating, and caching acorns, compared to less than 10% in 1983–1984 (Fig. 9). Estimated from the time-budget data, each territorial jay cached 5,000 to 7,000 acorns in a good acorn year and spent 16% of foraging time in January, 30.4% in February, and 43% in March recovering and eating them (Fig. 10). In the poor year jays spent less than 1.2% of their foraging time in January and February recovering acorns, and turned to less profitable foods, such as *Avena* grass seeds, and other foraging methods, such as searching through leaf litter, which has been shown to be energetically costly in Black-billed Magpies (*Pica hudsonia*; Mugaas and King 1981). Cached food may be crucial as the breeding season approaches. In good years, scrub-jays laid as early as 15 March, well before most invertebrates were abundant (see Fig. 4). Stored food may be specially important for incubating females that spent long periods on the nest. In another corvid, the Northwestern Crow (*Corvus caurinus*), James and Verbeek (1984) found that without cached food incubating females were unable to maintain normal incubation periods and spent long periods foraging.

Effect of acorn supplementation

Beginning in December 1983 and continuing through March following the acorn crop failure, I experimentally fed four pairs of jays 200 acorns per week. The acorns were placed on feeding platforms at the center of each territory, and the jays removed and stored them within 30 min. The time budgets of these jays closely matched those of jays during the good acorn years and were significantly different compared to unfed jays. For example, foraging time in January was 37% of total time for jays in the good years, and in the poor year 39% for experimentals and 62% for unfed jays; jays spent significantly more time foraging during the poor year (Kruskal-Wallis ANOVA, df = 2, χ^2 = 10.2, P < 0.01). The difference was due to the lack of readily available stored food; jays in good years spent 15.7% of their foraging time in January recovering stored acorns compared to 15.3% for experimentally fed jays and 1.2% for unfed jays in the poor year. These differences are probably even more pronounced in March, when in good years jays spent only 25% of their total time foraging and 43% of that foraging time recovering stored acorns. Unfortunately, I did not collect time budget data in March of the poor acorn year (1983).

Foraging of floaters

The foraging behavior of floaters was sampled from June 1981 through December 1982 (total N = 2987, minimum of 129 per month). This sample includes only juveniles in June and juveniles and older floaters in other months. No data were collected in May 1982 because all floaters disappeared.

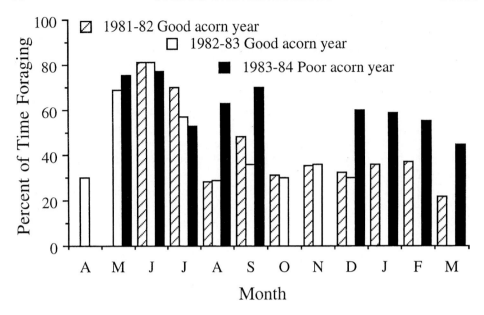

FIGURE 8. Percentage of time territorial scrub-jays spent foraging in two good acorn years and in one poor acorn year. Months without bars indicate no data were taken. Scrub-jays significantly increased their foraging time from August through March in the poor acorn year (Mann-Whitney U, P < 0.05 for each paired month). Total sample = 875 h, with a minimum of 18 h per month.

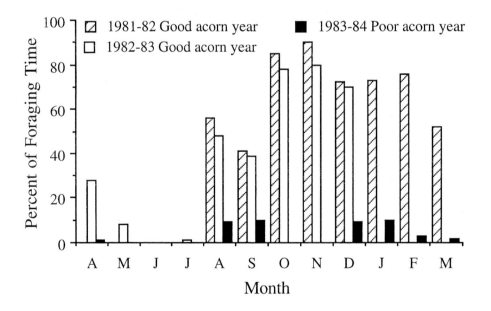

FIGURE 9. Percentage of foraging time territorial scrub-jays spent looking for, eating, caching, and recovering stored acorns in two good acorn years and a poor acorn year. Months without bars indicate no data were taken.

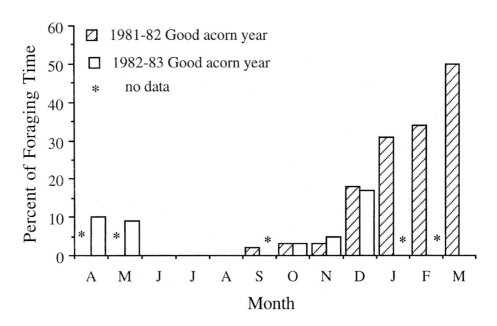

FIGURE 10. Percentage of foraging time territorial scrub-jays spent recovering and eating cached acorns and other cached food during the good acorn years (see text for explanation). Months without bars indicate no data were taken.

The foraging behavior of territorial adults and floaters is similar throughout the year (compare Figs. 7 and 11). The major difference is that young juveniles make heavy use of berries (blue elderberry, *Sambucus caerulea,* and fuschia-flowered gooseberry, *Ribes speciosum*), to which they directed 19% and 52% of total foraging activity in June and July, respectively. Floaters used acorns, stored food, and recovered food in nearly the same proportion as territorial jays and thus seem to be equally dependent on acorns. In 1982 and 1983, floaters disappeared from the study area beginning in April at about the time that territorial jays shifted from stored acorns to lepidopteran larvae. In 1985, when floaters did remain on the study area during the breeding season, foraging behavior of breeders and floaters was identical.

TERRITORIES AND TERRITORIAL BEHAVIOR

Aphelocoma jays are permanently territorial, and those unable to secure a territory are unable to breed. In cooperative species, nonbreeders delay dispersal, live in family groups on their natal territories, and help. In noncooperative populations, nonbreeders float. Differences in territorial behavior, habitat and habitat tolerance, variation in territory quality, and the degree of habitat saturation determine, in large part, the dispersal options available to newly independent young and older nonbreeders, and therefore play crucial roles in selecting for delayed or early dispersal.

TERRITORIAL BEHAVIOR

Scrub-jay breeders at Hastings rarely left their territories. In several thousand hours of field work I resighted 276 color-banded floaters 2,196 times, but I recorded breeders off their territories only 59 times. Of these, 33 (56%) occurred during the year of an acorn

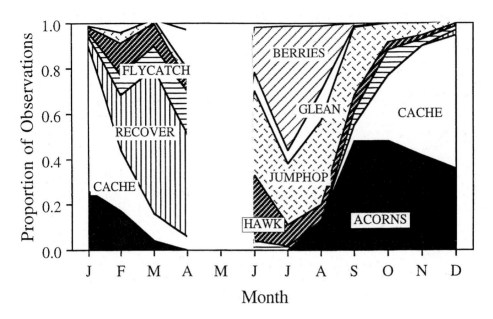

FIGURE 11. Seasonal change in foraging activities of nonbreeding floater scrub-jays, primarily first-year birds, over the year expressed as a proportion of all foraging activity (see text for explanation).

crop failure when jays abandoned their territories. Of the remaining 26, five were at water sources during July and August (see also Williams and Koenig 1980), 10 were at acorn-laden oaks in late winter, six were in large aggregations of floaters, three were in "power struggles" during mate replacements, one was in an unoccupied area with its fledglings, and three were off their territories for no discernable reason.

To quantify breeder movements and survivorship, I made quarterly surveys (see METHODS). Excluding the year of the acorn crop failure, only one individual (CR male), absent from its territory and counted as dead, later returned. In contrast, in 1983–1984 when the acorn crop failed, breeders began leaving in August. At first these movements were short and brief, with pairs joining into small groups in unoccupied habitat. Later in August up to 15 breeders and several nonbreeders formed loose groups that moved through both occupied and unoccupied areas, as breeders began abandoning their terri-tories. By December 1983, 57% (59 of 103) of the banded breeders could not be located, although 64% (38) subsequently returned, the majority in late March and early April. Males and females were equally likely to abandon their territories in the poor acorn year; of the 103 banded breeders present in summer of 1983 (55 males and 48 females), 30 males and 29 females were not found on their territories in December, and 20 males and 18 females later returned. Where acorns were available at higher elevations, breeders did not abandon their territories and floaters were common (pers. obs.). I sighted one of the banded absentee breeders in such an area.

Features of territorial interactions

Breeder-breeder territorial interactions and agonistic "*wek*" vocalizations in 1981–1982 are shown in Figure 12. *Wek* vocalizations were fewest in July and August, and most nu-merous in September and October when jays began harvesting large numbers of acorns and intrusions by floaters were common, whereas border interactions remained uniform over the year. Because scrub-jays remain aggressive toward their neighbors throughout the year, it appears that they are always at risk of losing all or part of their territories.

I emphasize that only territorial neighbors were evicted because unfamiliar territorial jays, like all floaters, were tolerated, at least during the nonbreeding season. For example, during August 1983, when some breeders abandoned their territories, male MB was observed for several hours over two consecutive days on the BURNT territory, 1.3 km distant. He was clearly visible to the residents, often foraging within 3 m, but was not challenged. Yet territorial neighbors, and even banded, known breeders from two territories distant, were quickly chased off.

Territorial interactions included vocalizations at borders, flight displays, and chases. These could be triggered simply by the approach of neighbors to a shared boundary as well as by active intrusion. Responses by the occupants could include any of the following: vocalization and body "pumping" on an exposed perch, flying to the border, "*wek*" vocalizations, "rattle" vocalizations (females only), display flights, supplants, and chases. Intrusions by neighbors were consistently met with agonistic behavior, followed by hasty retreat of the trespassers. Border disputes lasted from seconds to more than 30 min, and were substantially longer when new individuals were attempting to become established as breeders on adjacent territories. Neighboring pairs seemed to have specific areas where border disputes and territorial interactions were common and females frequently left the nest to participate.

Males were generally more aggressive, instigating the majority of interactions and continuing them longer. Territorial females were dominant over all other jays except their mates, including intruding neighboring males and adult male nonbreeding floaters.

Upon the death of a breeder, either sex was able to defend its territory prior to and

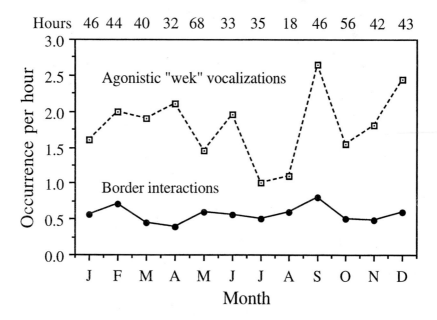

FIGURE 12. Rate of border interactions and aggressive "*wek*" vocalizations territorial scrub-jays directed towards territory neighbors. Numbers at top of figure are hours of observation of territorial scrub-jays.

during mate replacement, and both males and females quickly acquired new mates from the floater pool. Mate replacement varied from a quiet and increasingly close association between a resident and a new jay, with mutual courtship feeding over a several-day period leading to a closely bonded pair, to highly charged contests involving floaters, which resembled the "power struggles" described in the Acorn Woodpecker (*Melanerpes formicivorus*; Koenig 1981). Mate replacement could be extremely rapid, and I recorded most replacements after the fact. I witnessed six of the "quiet," and probably more common, replacements, and five "power struggles." The latter occurred in winter or early spring, when large numbers of floaters were nearby; up to 20 jays, primarily floaters, engaged in loud vocalizations, constant flights, including slow undulating display flights, chasing, contact, and even grappling to the ground. The participants, including the widowed bird, could carry on their dispute far from the territory of interest, and when they passed through other territories the residents also made undulating display flights, vocalized, and participated in the group melee. The nearly constant activity in these "power struggles" could last over two days, until a floater filled the breeding vacancy.

The pair bond and separation

Scrub-jays generally pair for life. I recorded 12 separations in 182 breeding-pair years (6.6%). However, if the sample is restricted to pairs in which both members were alive at the beginning of the next breeding season (a more critical measure of pair fidelity because it excludes mortality as a causative factor; Woolfenden and Fitzpatrick 1984), the separation index was 11.2%.

Of the 12 separations, five occurred during the fall or winter of the acorn crop failure, or early the following spring when birds returned to their territories. Some of the fall separations may really be territory abandonment. For example, female 2400R left her territory (and mate) in fall, and returned to the study area in April and paired with a different male; in her absence her former mate had paired with a neighboring territorial female. Excluding those observed in 1983–1984 leaves seven separations in 87 pair-years (8.0%).

Of these seven separations, five involved either: (1) adult, experienced breeders divorcing inexperienced or first-year mates to pair with experienced, established mates (two cases); (2) jays on intermittently occupied territories moving to adjacent permanently occupied territories (two cases); and (3) separation from an unsuccessful breeder (one case). Of the remaining two separations, one pair split their former territory and each acquired a new mate. In the other, a male separated from his mate and moved to and paired with a newly widowed female on the adjacent territory. Such divorces and movements may increase the reproductive success of the divorcer, as Baeyens (1981) showed for Eurasian Magpies (*Pica pica*).

Breeders and offspring

Prior to eight weeks postfledging, breeders actively fed young, and offspring remained in close associations with their parents. Offspring begged and followed adults, and near the end of the association males occasionally threatened or supplanted begging young. After eight weeks the young began wandering off, unaccompanied by parents, although some were fed up to 12 weeks after fledging. Territorial jays did not evict offspring (or unrelated floaters) from their territories until the onset of the following breeding season. In 875 h of time-budget observations (1981–1983) and 240 h following radio-tagged fledglings and juveniles (1985), I never observed parents in full chase of offspring in fall and winter; but in two interactions between breeders and their yearling offspring in May, the offspring were chased away. In approximately 50 h of nest watches, no offspring or other jays other than the pair were observed near nests or fledglings.

Breeders and floaters

The tolerance of independent offspring by breeders also extended to unrelated nonbreeders. As early as June, a few juveniles began wandering from their natal territories; these were ignored by other breeders, even those with young fledglings. By early July, loose aggregations of juvenile floaters were tolerated by breeders, who were still aggressive toward territorial neighbors, and from late July through April adult nonbreeding floaters also were tolerated.

The monthly rate of different types of aggressive interactions that breeders directed at nonbreeders (Table 1) was determined from time-budget observations, during which I estimated the number of floaters on the focal jay's territory every 10 to 20 min. As virtually all floaters disappeared from the study area in May–June of both 1982 and 1983, I have few data from the breeding season. However, during the nonbreeding season breeders used mostly low-level aggressive behaviors, such as "supplants," and few high-level aggressive behaviors such as "chases" or "chases off the territory." Most of the few interactions were a result of floaters either approaching too closely (< 1 m), or storing food in the same locations as the residents. Although floaters on territories tended to aggregate into loose groups of up to 20, even singles were tolerated or ignored during the nonbreeding season. My observations indicated that breeders preferentially supplanted unfamiliar floaters and, in effect, established dominance at first meeting, indicating that tolerance by breeders is based on subservient behavior of floaters. Floaters that remained on one or two territories for several months were rarely bothered.

Tolerance decreased as nest building began, and nests with eggs were defended. However, in every year floaters could be found on territories throughout April, even though the mean first egg date was 6 April. Although their disappearance in May coincided with increased aggression when breeders switched from supplants to long chases and chases off the territory (Fig. 13), many places existed on the study area where floaters could have settled at least temporarily, including some temporarily unoccupied

TABLE 1. TYPES AND FREQUENCIES OF AGGRESSIVE BEHAVIORS DIRECTED AT FLOATERS BY BREEDERS BY MONTH

Month	Hours observed	Floater-hours (FH)[a]	Supplant		Chase		Chase off	
			N	N/FH	N	N/FH	N	N/FH
Jan	46	444	94	0.21	41	0.0	3	0.01
Feb	44	394	99	0.25	26	0.07	1	0.02
Mar	40	242	90	0.37	23	0.09	4	0.02
April	32	105	38	0.36	15	0.14	12	0.12
May	68	<1	6	—	8	—	5	—
June	33	<<1	0	—	0	—	4	—
July	35	148	11	0.07	3	0.02	0	0
Aug	18	141	21	0.14	9	0.06	0	0
Sept	46	219	63	0.29	37	0.17	3	0.01
Oct	56	213	100	0.47	33	0.15	4	0.02
Nov	42	343	141	0.41	59	0.17	4	0.01
Dec	43	383	136	0.36	29	0.08	0	0

[a] FH = floater-hour: mean number of floaters on the territory during each observation hour, summed over the total number of observation hours.

territories. In addition, large aggregations of floaters disappeared from temporarily unoccupied territories where they were free from disturbance by breeders.

In May and June of most years, floaters were evicted from territories. In 1985, however, many floaters remained on the study area and breeders were more tolerant (interactions not quantified) as long as they remained away from the nests, territory centers, and the residents. This is similar to the interactions between Florida Scrub-Jay breeders and helpers prior to when helpers feed the nestlings (G. Woolfenden, pers. comm.). This extended period of tolerance occurred in a year when acorns remained available on the oaks well into May. During May and June 1985, 93% of 914 locations of 11 radio-collared floaters occurred on territories, mostly near the margins.

Why do breeders defend against neighbors during the nonbreeding season but tolerate floaters? First, a small investment in territorial defense throughout the year prevents neighbors from usurping territory space, a real threat as shown during the acorn crop failure; in at least three cases jays that abandoned their territories failed to recoup them the following spring because neighboring pairs that remained took them over. Second, tolerance of floaters suggests that exclusivity of territorial space is not critical during the nonbreeding season, but floaters are easily expelled at the onset of the breeding season through the dominance established earlier.

TERRITORY ACQUISITION

To gain a territory and breeding status, juveniles and older floaters have three options: (1) to pair with an established breeder upon the death of its mate; (2) to pair with another floater and establish a territory de novo; or (3) to pair and establish a territory in an unoccupied area. Option 1 was used by 62 of 90 (69%) jays, options 2 and 3 by 15% each.

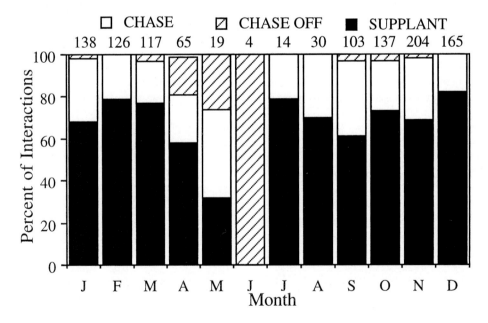

FIGURE 13. Seasonal change in aggressive behaviors breeders directed at floaters. Numbers above bars are total number of interactions recorded in each month.

First-year jays acquired territories almost exclusively by pairing with established adults. In five years (215 breeding-pair years), only one pair of first-year jays successfully defended a territory throughout a breeding season. In five other cases, first-year males established temporary, small, and intermittently defended "pseudo-territories" that overlapped portions of two or three adjacent territories. The males paired with first-year females and three pairs built nests, but never laid eggs. The pairs were dominant over floaters but not over the neighboring, true territory holders. In every case by early May, the females disappeared, followed shortly by the males. One of the five males was the offspring of an adjacent territorial pair; the other four were banded as juveniles and were not natal to the study area. Four of the five males returned to the same area the following autumn and reestablished their pseudo-territories and paired with a first-year female. Again the pairs failed to lay and defend or remain on their territories through May. Three of these five males returned and eventually acquired true territories, two as three-year olds and one at age four. In two cases, the territories claimed included the original pseudo-territory.

The age at which true territories are acquired is a crucial demographic variable. While a complete analysis is given below, here I present data for calculating this variable. The sample includes novice jays filling territories using all three options listed above. On established territories only replacements of banded breeders were included. Figure 14a gives the age distribution of these jays, separating exact and minimum ages. In Figure 14b, the data are presented with jays in the minimum age classes placed in the distribution in proportion to the exact age jays. For example, of the 14 females in the 2+ age category in Fig. 14a, 66% were placed in the age 2 category and 34% in the age 3 category in Fig. 14b, representing the proportion of two- and three-year old females in the sample whose age was known exactly. This underestimates the age of jays filling the vacancies, but provides conservative figures for later calculations.

Many jays did not acquire a territory for several years and females filled vacancies at a younger age than males. But are these jays really novice territory holders? One complication is that breeders occasionally shift territories, most often a result of death of a mate or divorce, which could result in misclassifying a new arrival as a novice. If one counts unbanded breeders that moved into the study area as first-time territory holders, the age distribution may be artificially shifted to older age classes. Of 57 vacancies filled by jays ≥ 2 years old (thus excluding yearlings), breeders filled 20, of which 15 were on adjacent territories; 11 of the 20 occurred during the acorn crop failure. Of the 20 vacancies filled by established breeders, 15 (75%) moved to an adjoining territory. Three long-distance movements occurred during the acorn crop failure; the longest one was three intervening territories. Excluding the 11 cases during the crop failure, 88% of movements by breeders were to adjacent territories, and 100% within only one intervening territory. Throughout the study, I periodically searched nearby locations, including at least one territory beyond the study area. Only one former breeder was found, a male that had disappeared during the acorn crop failure. If movement by breeders onto the study area is as rare as movement off, the bias imposed by possible long-distance movement of breeders in calculating the age at onset of breeding is negligible.

Another method for determining age of first breeding is by following the fate of banded nestlings. Of those banded as nestlings in 1981–1983 that eventually acquired territories on the study area (N = 12), 42% did so their first year, 33% their second, and 25% their third (Table 2).

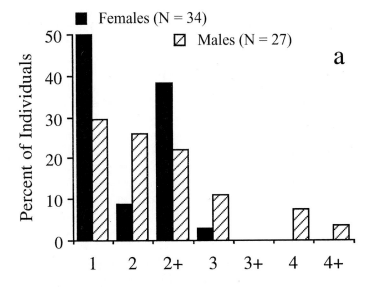

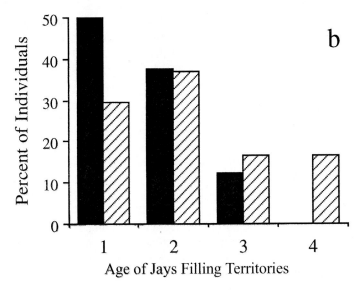

Age of Jays Filling Territories

FIGURE 14. Age distribution of first-time breeders filling territory vacancies: a) age distribution includes exact and minimum ages; b) age distribution with minimum age scrub-jays included in age categories in proportion to the distribution of exact age scrub-jays filling territories.

TERRITORY CHARACTERISTICS

Between March and August over five breeding seasons I mapped 194 territories and determined territory size; maps were made in the period from nest building through dispersal of young. In 1981 the study area encompassed 83 ha and I mapped 23 territories. From 1982–1985 it was 173 ha and held from 40 (1984) to 53 (1982) territories (Figs. 15–19).

TABLE 2. Age at which scrub-jays hatched on the study area (1981–1983) first acquired a territory

Year hatched	Number independent	Number acquiring breeding status in				Total	Unaccounted
		1982	1983	1984	1985		
1981	33	3	1	1	0	5	28
1982	54	—	2	3	2	7	47
1983	23	—	—	0	1	1	22
Total	110					13	97

Jays breeding at age (year)	N	(%)	Males	Females
1	5	(38%)	2	3
2	5	(38%)	2	3
3	3	(23%)	3	0

Territory size and population density

The 194 territories averaged 2.53 ha, and ranged from 0.66 to 6.5 ha. Average territory sizes were smaller in 1981 through 1983 (range 2.16–2.46 ha), increased significantly in 1984 (3.18 ha), and then decreased significantly in 1985 (2.64 ha; ANOVA, F = 5.62, df = 5, 205, P < 0.001; Fisher's LSD test, P < 0.05; Table 3).

Breeder density ranged from 9.2 pairs/40 ha in 1984 to 12.2 pairs/40 ha in 1982 (Table 3). Mean territory size was inversely related to breeder population density (Fig. 20). The relative stability in both the number of territories and territory size in the first three years of the study contrasts with 1984 (after the acorn crop failure) when many territories were abandoned and the number of territories decreased 20% and mean territory size held by breeders increased 57% (Table 3). In 1985, five new territories were established and the average size decreased 17%. Despite this fluctuation, the area actually covered by territories remained essentially unchanged at 60 to 66% throughout the study.

Habitat features: habitat suitability and territory quality

Despite the change in breeder density and number of territories, four habitat types were consistently avoided: (1) dense mixed hardwood forest; (2) coast range blue oak foothill woodland; (3) large unbroken areas of chaparral; and (4) sparse coast valley oak foothill woodland. Jays whose territories included portions of these habitats did use adjacent areas of chaparral, blue oak woodland, or oak savannah on occasion, but rarely mixed hardwood, open grassland, and oak savannah. Comparisons of vegetation attributes between scrub-jay territories and the study area as a whole, unoccupied areas only, and each of the four habitat-types scrub-jays avoid, revealed that preferred habitat consists of patches with intermediate oak density and canopy cover, interspersed with

TABLE 3. Study area size, territory size, breeder density, and area occupied (ha), 1981–1985

Year	Study area (ha)	Number of territories	Mean territory size (ha)	Pairs/40 ha	Area occupied, ha (%)
1981	83	23	2.46	11.1	—[a]
1982	173	53	2.16	12.2	103.6 (60%)
1983	173	50	2.37	11.5	113.6 (66%)
1984	173	40	3.18	9.2	114.3 (66%)
1985	173	45	2.64	10.4	113.5 (65%)
Mean ± SD:			2.59 ± 0.4	10.9 ± 1.1	111.3 ± 5.1

[a] Area occupied could not be accurately calculated for 1981.

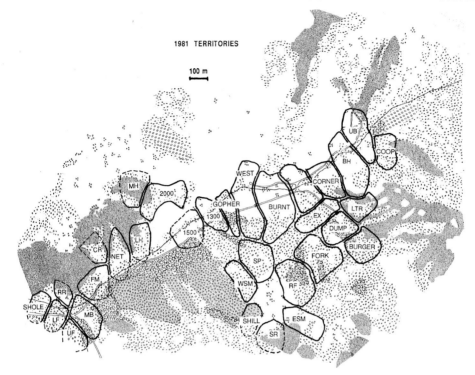

FIGURE 15. Location of scrub-jay territories in 1981. Vegetation key as in Figure 2.

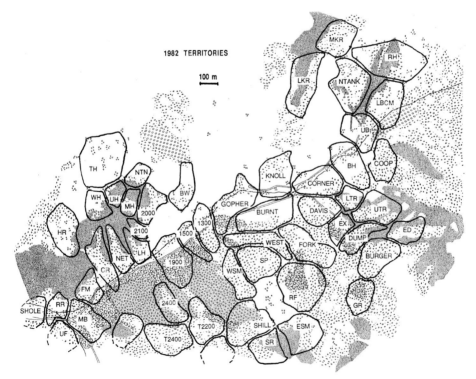

FIGURE 16. Location of scrub-jay territories in 1982. Vegetation key as in Figure 2.

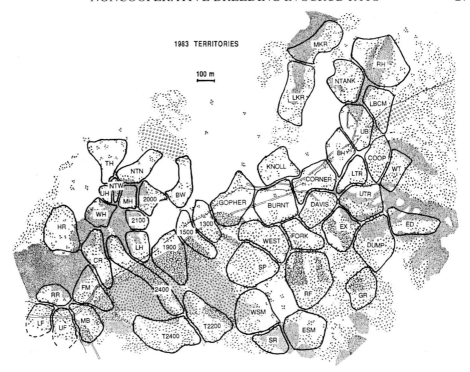

FIGURE 17. Location of scrub-jay territories in 1983. Vegetation key as in Figure 2.

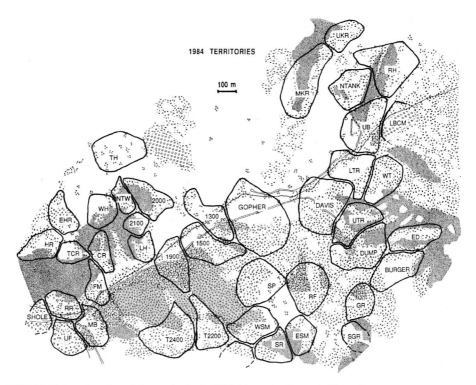

FIGURE 18. Location of scrub-jay territories in 1984. Vegetation key as in Figure 2.

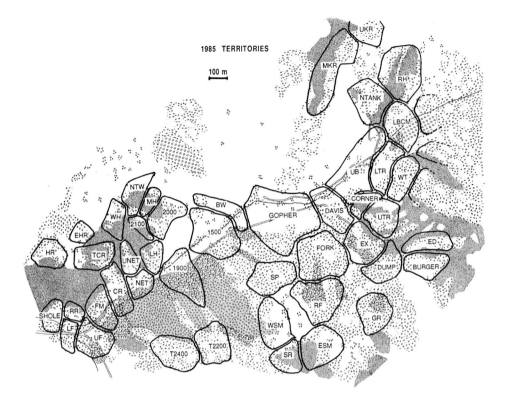

FIGURE 19. Location of scrub-jay territories in 1985. Vegetation key as in Figure 2.

shrubs and open areas, that is, a mosaic of grassland, scrub, and woodland vegetation. Both breeders and floaters avoid habitats where tree or shrub density and cover is high (occupied by Steller's Jays, *Cyanocitta stelleri*), as well as habitats that are too open (Table 4, Fig. 21). These latter habitats are avoided by nonbreeding floaters as well.

Analysis of territory quality

To analyze the characteristics that contribute to territory quality, I selected variables that could be measured with a digital planimeter from large scale aerial photographs (1 cm = 12.5 m). On 24 territories I measured area of total territory size, oak canopy, other tree canopy, grassland, chaparral, and other brush. The measurements were converted to percentages and arcsin transformed for subsequent analysis.

Occupancy rate was used as an indicator of territory quality. Territories in high-quality habitat should be occupied longer and more consistently, due to higher survivorship and immigration. Rating scrub-jay territories by occupancy rate is not as clear-cut as in species such as Acorn Woodpeckers, where territories are based on availability of granaries and are either occupied or not (Koenig and Mumme 1987). In scrub-jays, space itself is important, and territories may join, split, disappear, or be created de novo, complicating a direct calculation of percent of time a territory is occupied. Also, because territory boundaries may change, the "same" territory may include different resources in different years, obscuring relationships between quality and occupancy. To overcome some of these problems, I modified Koenig and Mumme's three-tier classification as follows:

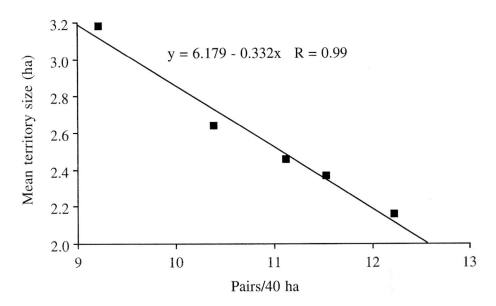

FIGURE 20. Relationship between mean territory size and mean breeder density (1981–1985).

Type 1: Territory always occupied; the size and boundaries remained constant over the study period (N = 11).

Type 2: Not continuously occupied and the boundaries varied (i.e., when a territorial pair died or left, the space was taken over by neighbors). This category is arbitrary because changes may reflect death or movement of breeders due either to poor quality habitat or chance (N = 8).

Type 3: Not continuously occupied as a unit and not used in every year; i.e., when not occupied, neighboring territorial pairs did not occupy and defend the space (N = 5).

A discriminant function analysis (DFA) found significant differences between the three territory types ($\chi^2 = 22.1$, df = 8, P < 0.005) and classified 79% correctly based on four of the original variables. In decreasing importance these were: area of shrubs, area of oak canopy, percent cover of grassland, and percent cover of oak canopy. Only one Type 1 territory was misclassified (the RF territory) as a Type 2, whereas two Type 2 were classified as Type 3, and two Type 3 as Type 2.

TABLE 4. VEGETATION ATTRIBUTES (MEAN ± SD) OF OCCUPIED TERRITORIES COMPARED TO THOSE OF THE STUDY AREA AS A WHOLE, THOSE OF UNOCCUPIED HABITATS AS A WHOLE, AND THOSE OF UNOCCUPIED OAK SAVANNAH, CHAPARRAL, BLUE OAK WOODLAND (BOW), AND MIXED HARDWOOD (MHW) HABITAT

Type	N	Proportion of		DBH trees (cm)	Number of oaks	Number of species of oaks
		Shrub	Canopy			
Territories	111	0.15 ± 0.19	0.23 ± 0.17	0.74 ± 0.85	6.6 ± 7.5	1.7 ± 0.80
All plots	247	0.19 ± 0.20*	0.21 ± 0.19	0.66 ± 0.90	6.5 ± 8.1	1.4 ± 0.91*
Unoccupied	136	0.22 ± 0.13**	0.18 ± 0.12	0.59 ± 0.56	6.5 ± 0.6	1.2 ± 0.71***
Oak-savannah	38	0.01 ± 0.04***	0.06 ± 0.01***	0.32 ± 0.49***	2.7 ± 0.4***	0.6 ± 0.94**
Chaparral	30	0.90 ± 0.18	0.10 ± 0.03***	0.13 ± 0.36***	0.3 ± 1.0***	0.3 ± 0.76**
BOW	36	0.01 ± 0.04***	0.32 ± 0.15**	0.91 ± 0.63	12.3 ± 15.6***	1.8 ± 0.74
MHW	31	0.09 ± 0.19	0.35 ± 0.17***	1.10 ± 0.60*	12.6 ± 7.0***	2.1 ± 0.69

Notes: Statistical tests of differences among attributes of territories and other categories by t-test (with percentages arc-sine transformed) except comparisons of mean number of oaks and number of oak species by Mann-Whitney U. *P < 0.05 **P < 0.01 ***P < 0.001

Chaparral | Valley Oak Savannah | Blue Oak Woodland | Mixed Hardwood Forest

SCRUB-JAY HABITAT SCRUB-JAY HABITAT SCRUB-JAY HABITAT

FIGURE 21. Schematic representation of habitat types and plant communities on the study area illustrating preferred, occupied scrub-jay habitat.

The amount and spacing of shrubs, which provide nest sites and cover, was by far the most important variable. Type 1 territories contained more shrubs (mean of 0.90 vs. 0.39 and 0.26 ha for Types 1, 2 and 3, respectively; Table 5). Of the five Type 3 territories, two had no shrubs, one had 0.01 ha, one had 0.1 ha, and the fifth 1.2 ha, the latter misclassified by the DFA as a Type 2 territory. The lack of shrub cover evidently explains why unoccupied areas that appeared suitable, such as the large area of blue oak woodland between the GR and RF territories (see territory maps, Figs. 15–19), were not used. Percentages of grass and of oak canopy were greatest on Type 3 territories (Table 5), suggesting that extensive open grassland and dense woodland habitats are avoided.

Territory size varied in relation to several variables. Partial correlation analysis indicates that area of grassland was positively correlated with territory size ($R = 0.60$, $P = 0.003$), again indicating that open grassland does not provide suitable resources. No relationship was found between area of shrub cover and territory size. Oak canopy—a critical resource for jays—did not vary independently with territory size; a minimum of 0.16 ha occurred on even the smallest territories. However, overall oak density and number of oak species are not evenly distributed; while all territories included at least two species, some territories held predominately one species and others three. Because *Q. agrifolia* retains acorns for much longer periods, it is a relatively more valuable resource. Because oak species tend to produce crops synchronously, and variation in production is high even within species (Carmen et al. 1987, Koenig et al. 1994b), territories with greater numbers of oak species and individual trees are more likely to produce good acorn crops in any given year.

DISPERSAL AND FLOATING

Knowledge of the behavior of floaters is essential to understanding the evolution of reproductive strategies (Stutchbury and Robertson 1986). Rather than being merely a

TABLE 5. CHARACTERISTICS OF TERRITORIES (MEANS ± SD) OF HIGH (TYPE 1), MEDIUM (TYPE 2), AND LOW QUALITY (TYPE 3)

	Type 1	Type 2	Type 3
N	11	8	5
Size (ha)	2.8 ± 1.7	2.0 ± 1.0	2.8 ± 0.9
Canopy oaks (ha)	0.68 ± 0.48	0.48 ± 0.40	0.83 ± 0.37
Area shrub (ha)	0.90 ± 0.43	0.39 ± 0.21	0.25 ± 0.51
Area grass (ha)	1.2 ± 1.1	1.1 ± 0.8	1.6 ± 1.2
Proportion canopy	0.24 ± 0.13	0.23 ± 0.12	0.35 ± 0.23
Proportion shrub	0.39 ± 0.14	0.32 ± 0.21	0.17 ± 0.26
Proportion grass	0.40 ± 0.14	0.50 ± 0.17	0.55 ± 0.29

Note: Territory quality classified by occupancy rate during study period, 1982-1985.

surplus, floaters may show complex social organization and exhibit various strategies to become breeders (Smith 1978, 1984), which in turn affects the behavior of existing territorial breeders. For example, females in Red-winged Blackbirds (*Agelaius phoeniceus*) defend territories against nonbreeding females (Hurly and Robertson 1984). The presence of floaters in Bank Swallows (*Riparia riparia*) induces males to mate-guard (Beecher and Beecher 1979), and in Eastern Bluebirds (*Sialia sialis*) they affect seasonal patterns of territorial behavior (Gowaty 1985). Floaters can evict male and female territorial tropical House Wrens (*Troglodytes aedon*; Freed 1986) and male Song Sparrows (*Melospiza melodia*; Arcese 1987), but floaters do not challenge territorial Rufous-collared Sparrows (*Zonotrichia capensis*; Smith 1984). Floaters may live singly, sneaking through territories as do male Song Sparrows (Arcese 1987) and both sexes of Rufous-collared Sparrows (Smith 1978), or in aggregations off territorially held areas (Atwood 1980a). Within groups, the status of floaters may determine their access to resources and chance of eventually breeding (Eden 1987; Smith 1978, 1984). Floaters may also engage in extrapair copulations as shown in Tree Swallows (*Tachycineta bicolor*) and may be responsible for at least some extrapair young (Barber and Robertson 1999).

Given the diversity and importance of floater behavior and social organization, the first step in assessing the trade-offs between early independent breeding, delayed dispersal and helping, and floating, is acquiring detailed data on dispersal and movement patterns. Especially important are parent-offspring and breeder-nonbreeder interactions, the types of habitats available for dispersing individuals, and the social relationships among nonbreeders. Such detailed data are available for nonbreeders of cooperative species, including Florida Scrub-Jays (e.g., Woolfenden and Fitzpatrick 1984, Fitzpatrick and Woolfenden 1986) and Mexican Jays (Brown 1963, 1970; Brown and Brown 1984), but are rare for noncooperative species (Smith and Arcese 1989). Most commonly, floater presence is inferred from replacement of breeders (Watson and Moss 1970, Rutberg and Rohwer 1980, Sæther and Fonstad 1981, Stutchbury and Robertson 1986). Floaters have been found in a few cooperative breeders, such as Red-cockaded Woodpeckers (*Picoides borealis*; Walters 1990), Acorn Woodpeckers (Koenig and Mumme 1987), Mexican Jays (Brown 1986), Hoatzins (*Opisthocomus hoatzin*; Strahl and Schmitz 1990), Groove-billed Anis (*Crotophaga sulcirostris*; Koford et al. 1990), Pukekos (*Porphyrio porphyrio*; Craig and Jamieson 1990), and White-throated Magpie-Jays (*Calocitta formosa*; Innes and Johnston 1996, Langen 1996b). However, floaters (when their numbers were estimated) comprised less than 5% of these populations and appear either to be "losers" (*sensu* Fitzpatrick and Woolfenden 1988) or the product of chance events rather than individuals exercising a viable alternative dispersal strategy. (Alternatively, floaters in these and other cooperative breeders may be difficult to detect and monitor, as is the case in most noncooperative species). An interesting exception is the Australian Magpie (*Gymnorhina tibicen*), in which delayed dispersal and floating are both conspicuously expressed dispersal options (Carrick 1972). In studies that explicitly compared closely related cooperative and noncooperative species, floaters were rarely, if ever, seen (Zack and Ligon 1985a,b; Bell and Ford 1986) or not followed in any detail (Atwood 1980a, Leighton 1986).

In the following discussion, "juvenile dispersal" is defined as the initial, usually one-way, movement away from the natal territory, as contrasted with individual "movements" of independent floaters either on defined home-ranges or directionally over long distances.

JUVENILE DISPERSAL

In 1984, I radio tracked three juvenile scrub-jay males from two territories. Two male fledglings from UB territory (jays 570 and 025) and one male from 1300 territory (jay 640) were fitted with radio backpacks five weeks after fledging. The jays were followed until the transmitters failed, from four to eight weeks later. Focal animal point samples every 10 min (Altmann 1974) on each individual lasted 3 h, and morning, midday, and evening watches over a one- or two-day period were combined for composite full-day samples. During the watches the jays' foraging behavior, microhabitat use, behavioral interactions, and location were monitored. I collected 13 representative full-day watches on jay 640 (114 h), 8 days on 025 (72 h), and 6 days on 570 (54 h).

The movements of jays 570 and 640 illustrate the salient points of juvenile dispersal (Figs. 22 and 23). Each map represents a full-day sample consisting of three 3-h samples with a total of 57 location points; hence, both home range and activity centers can be identified. Prior to six weeks post-fledging juveniles associated closely with parents and remained on their natal territories (jay 570, Fig. 22a, and jay 640, Fig. 23a). Between six and eight weeks, the fledglings began wandering onto adjacent territories unaccompanied by their parents (Figs. 22b,c and Fig. 23b). After two months, juveniles either moved between their natal and other territories, remained on their natal territories (Fig 22d), or departed permanently (jay 640, Fig. 23c). When off their natal territories the three jays used other territories almost exclusively, with less than 2% of their activity in unoccupied areas (Table 6).

When on territories, the tagged jays and other floaters appeared to have free access to all areas, including former nest sites (marked by hollow squares in the figures). Breeders were dominant over floaters, including breeding females over floater males, and first-year breeders over older floaters. Floaters were not restricted to territory edges or interstitial areas.

A larger but less precise sample based on 340 resightings of 51 juveniles banded as nestlings just prior to and following dispersal indicate that both males and females may remain near or on their natal territories for extended periods. For example, females 37 and 62 fledged on BURNT and DAVIS territories, respectively, in 1981 were recorded at 47 and 36 locations between five and 24 weeks post-fledging; 27% for female 37 were on her natal territory, compared to 10% for female 62. Over 97% of all locations for these two jays were on territories. Note that all of these examples are for jays remaining on

TABLE 6. PERCENTAGE OF RADIO LOCATIONS OF THREE MALE JUVENILES ON NATAL, NON-NATAL, AND OFF TERRITORIES, JULY–SEPTEMBER 1984 (NUMBER OF LOCATIONS IN PARENTHESES)

	Sample sizes			Prior to 6 weeks post-fledging			6 weeks to 2 months post-fledging			2 to 3 months post-fledging		
Jay	hours	locations	NL[a]	natal	other[b]	off[c]	natal	other	off	natal	other	off
640	114	686	32	100% (140)	0	0	48% (50)	43% (45)	9% (9)	1% (4)	97% (399)	2% (7)
570	54	327	28	100% (97)	0	0	88% (44)	12% (6)	0	59% (90)	41% (62)	0
025	72	416	33	97% (180)	3% (5)	0	77% (77)	22% (23)	1% (2)	4% (4)	95% (92)	1% (1)

[a] Not located precisely.
[b] Non-natal territories.
[c] Unoccupied (non-territorial) areas.

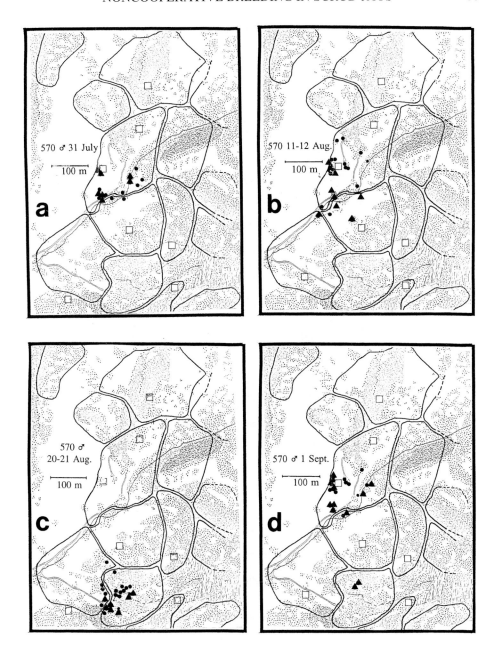

FIGURE 22. Radio-tracked dispersal of male 570 from its natal territory. Circles indicate one location, triangles ≥2 locations (N = 57 locations), open squares represent nest locations, and solid lines territory boundaries. Radio locations (a) 6 weeks (all locations on natal UB territory), (b) 7 weeks, (c) 8 weeks, and (d) 9 weeks after fledging.

the study area but that 63% of all young banded as nestlings and reaching independence were not resighted. Jays often disperse considerable distances during this initial period, as shown by the number of floaters detected and the long-distance movements recorded for three first-year birds.

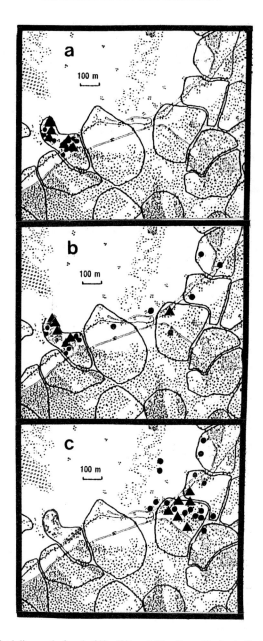

FIGURE 23. Radio-tracked dispersal of male 640 off its natal territory. Circles indicate one location, triangles ≥2 locations (N = 57 locations), and solid lines territory boundaries. Radio locations (a) 6 weeks (locations shown on map of the entire study area), (b) 7 weeks, and (c) 10 weeks after fledging.

FLOATER MOVEMENTS AND DISPERSION PATTERNS IN THE NONBREEDING SEASON

Monthly surveys from late July 1981 to early May 1982, both in areas occupied by breeders and in areas without territories, revealed an uneven distribution of floaters (Fig. 24). Floaters aggregated loosely in three distinct locations on the study area: on the MB, LF, RR territories; on the 2000R, MH, and NTN territories; and on the area circumscribed by the GOPHER, EX, and NTANK territories (see territory maps, Figs. 16–19, for specific territory locations). The mean number per aggregation over the 9-month period was 10 and ranged from 2 to 30. On surveys and during incidental field work, floaters were rarely seen in unoccupied areas, or on more than the few territories that were consistently used by them.

Floaters formed aggregations beginning in July as they reached independence and began to disperse from their natal territories. A fledgling's recruitment to a particular aggregation appeared to determine its initial dispersal distance. If aggregations formed on a fledgling's natal territory, the fledgling tended to remain in the vicinity. For example, radiotagged jays 570 and 025 fledged from UB Territory in 1984. Jay 570 joined an aggregation centered on the UB and UBCM territories, and so spent a major portion of the year on its natal territory (see Fig. 22d). On the other hand, jay 025 joined an aggregation on the EX territory, 1.0 km away, and was not detected subsequently on UB.

The same pattern of floater distribution occurred in the nonbreeding season (late July to late April) in 1982–1983 and 1984–1985. In 1983–1084, the anomalous year, all juveniles dispersed from the study area and no floaters immigrated in fall or winter; at least 33% of banded breeders also abandoned their territories in the fall and did not return until the following spring. In 1983–1984 floaters aggregated at higher elevations where acorns were abundant, as close as 4 km to the study area. No floaters were seen on the study area until March 1984, when many of the territorial breeders were returning.

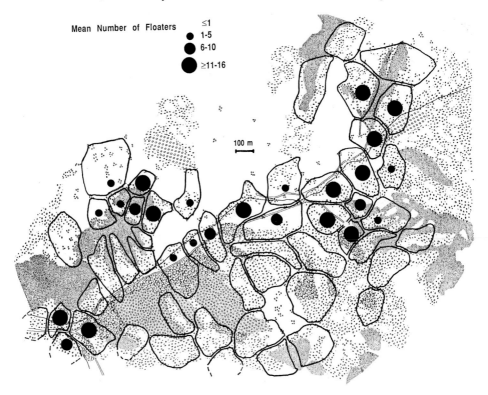

FIGURE 24. Mean numbers and distribution of floaters on the study area during the nonbreeding season 1981–1982. Data are the mean from monthly surveys of territories and unoccupied areas from August through April. Solid lines are 1982 territory boundaries; territories lacking dots indicate no floater use.

Based on periodic surveys, in three of four years the study area had the largest floater population within several kilometers, and must have attracted floaters from a wide area. Other isolated aggregations were located in the vicinity of the study area, each separated by extensive areas with no floaters. Because floaters move widely, it was difficult to estimate their numbers. For example, of 350 jays banded as floaters, 120 (32%) were never resighted, suggesting that many were merely passing through the study area. However, periodic surveys on the study area of 194 ha indicated a rough mean during the late summer to early spring period of 100 in 1981–1982, 120 in 1982–1983, <5 in 1983–1984, and 40 in 1984–1985. An estimated December population of 100 floaters on the study area in 1981 represented juveniles from about 160 territories, based upon a mean of 1.2 fledglings per pair and survivorship of 52%.

Stability of aggregations

In 1981–1982 virtually all (>90%) of the floaters in several aggregations were color-banded. An analysis of the resightings on the BURNT and BH territories illustrates the stability of the aggregations and the localized movements of floaters. On the BURNT territory I banded 75 floaters and resighted 53 there from July 1981 to early May 1982. By mid-January a core group had formed; in eight surveys seven to 10 days apart from 1 February to 1 May, only 17 banded individuals were recorded (366 total observations). Twelve of the 17 were seen on six or more of the eight surveys, and pooling the resightings of these 17, the probability of finding one of the core group on BURNT was 0.72. During this three-month period, on 21 other occasions only four other banded individuals and four unbanded jays were seen. Prior to 1 February, 37% (63) of the 170 resightings of the 17 core-group members occurred on BURNT, compared to 71% (140) of 196 later.

Resightings and surveys on neighboring territories, also with large numbers of floaters, revealed a similar level of stabilization in movements and indicated that transfers between the aggregations were infrequent (distances between foci of aggregations varied from 100 m to 2 km). Between July and May of 1981–1982, I recorded 604 resightings of 65 individuals on the BH and UB territories, which were one to two territories distant from BURNT, respectively. Of the 17 BURNT floaters only five were seen a total of 19 times on the BH and UB territories, with one individual seen 14 times. Floaters from BURNT were mostly resighted on adjacent territories. Occasional long-distance movements were observed when singles joined other aggregations. Most of these longer forays occurred in late autumn, and only two of the 17 core individuals at BURNT were observed after 1 February in other groups; both were in an area 1.6 km distant, where they had been originally banded in early fall. These data show a tendency of jays in localized groups to wander varying distances, and this tendency is probably a part of a continuum of seasonally varying longer distance movements.

Home range and habitat use in winter

Radio telemetry was used to acquire data on floater home range and habitat use, and to ascertain if dispersal forays are made out of the aggregations. Two females (jays 680 and 695) not hatched on the study area were radio-tracked in November and December of 1984. Locations for jay 695 covered 5 December to 11 January, with eight composite days (72 h total). Locations on 680 extended from 5 to 23 December, with four composite days (36 h total). Figure 25 illustrates typical patterns of habitat and use of local territories for each jay over one composite day (9 h, 57 location points).

Jays 680 and 695 spent 88% (N = 198 sample points) and 99% (N = 433 sample points) of the sample period on territories. Eleven locations for 695 off the study area are excluded from the percentages. Female 695 typically ranged over a far greater area and used nine territories vs. five for jay 680. Over the entire sample period, jay 680 used seven territories with a home range of 8.8 hectares; jay 695 used 11 with a home range of 26.0 hectares. However, the radio lasted longer on jay 695, and her movements were followed longer. If concurrent sample periods are compared, the differences are smaller (8.8 vs. 11.3 ha).

Floater locations indicate that they had free access to all areas and were not shunted away from nest sites or onto territory boundaries. Resightings of color-banded floaters of both sexes indicate a similar pattern of home range use and home range size and use in winter.

Home ranges of floaters in aggregations overlapped considerably, and individuals showed consistent home-range use during the winter. Floaters covered a much larger area than the average breeder's territory (mean floater home range = 21 ha, based on two radio-tagged jays and resightings of 11 jays each with over 20 locations; mean breeder territory size = 2.5 hectares, N = 194).

FLOATER MOVEMENTS AND DISPERSION PATTERNS DURING THE BREEDING SEASON

The distribution of floaters during the breeding season varied considerably. In 1981–1982 and 1982–1983 large numbers immigrated onto the study area during the fall and winter, and then abruptly disappeared by May. In 1983–1984 (year of the poor acorn crop), no floaters were seen on the study area during winter. A few returned in spring and were seen sporadically during the breeding season. In 1984–1985, floaters again immigrated into the study area, and these and many jays hatched there in 1984 remained

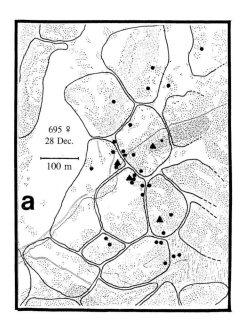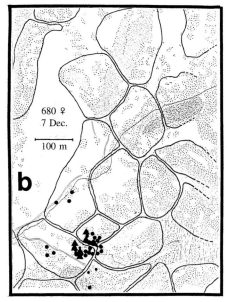

FIGURE 25. Radio-locations and winter home range use by two radio-collared first-year female floaters. Circles indicate one location, triangles ≥2 locations (N = 57 locations), and solid lines territory boundaries. (a) Female 695, and (b) Female 680.

throughout the breeding season. These results are given in greater detail in the following paragraphs and the sequences of dispersal are diagrammed in Figure 26.

In 1981–1982, the approximately 100 floaters on the study area were easily located during the nonbreeding season until they abruptly disappeared in late April 1982. Of 214 banded in 1981–1982, 148 were resighted 1,575 times during the fall, winter, and early spring. But between 1 May and 30 June 1982, only six were observed once each on the study area. Two were on territories in the first week of May where they had been seen frequently during the previous winter months. Three others were males who earlier had established "pseudo-territories" and had been seen in unoccupied habitat nearby. The remaining individual came to traps baited with acorns on the WSM territory. Sightings of unbanded and unidentified floaters were equally rare, despite 1,500+ field hours during the breeding season. Floaters seen during this time, both on and off territories, were silent and inconspicuous, in contrast to their behavior in other months. Indeed, those on territories were usually first observed when they were chased off by breeders.

In early July 1982, newly independent juveniles began wandering off their natal territories and joined aggregations. By late July, older floaters began reappearing in these aggregations as the breeders became tolerant of them. A total of 15 banded adult floaters (11 males, 4 females) returned to the study area out of a possible 214 pre-reproductives (nestlings and floaters) banded prior to the 1982 breeding season. Three were natal to the study area, and nine eventually bred there (three the following spring of 1983, and six in 1984 or 1985; Fig. 26).

A similar pattern was observed in 1982–1983; large numbers of floaters immigrated onto the study area in the fall of 1982 and of 71 banded, 43 were resighted a total of 275 times. In addition, of 54 jays banded as nestlings in 1982 and reaching independence, 16 were resighted as floaters. Floaters remained on territories somewhat longer in 1983, with 30 on the LF/RR territory on 5 May. Between 1 May and 30 June, 13 banded individuals were resighted 15 times. Of those, six were observed between 1–5 May on territories, and four others had established pseudo-territories and were seen in unoccupied areas nearby; of the remainder, three were seen sneaking through a territory and one was in an unoccupied area. Of the 71 floaters banded as immigrants plus 16 jays natal to the study area resighted between fall and early spring, nine (seven males and two females) returned after July. Six of the nine were natal to the study area and six eventually bred on the study area; 3 in 1984 and 3 in 1985 (Fig. 26). Thus the floaters that did return, predominantly males that fledged on the study area, had a high probability of breeding there. This suggests that philopatry, or at least persistence in a familiar area, coupled with age-related dominance, facilitates acquisition of breeding space.

Breeder aggression towards floaters increased during nest building and egg laying, and coincided with the disappearance of floaters. However, floaters also left areas in which they were not disturbed. Two cases are illustrative.

Part of BURNT territory, along Big Creek, was occupied by a stable group of 17 floaters from January through April 1982. The breeders laid their first egg on 2 April and nested 75 m from the activity area of the floaters. The floaters were excluded from the nest area, but in 23 h of observation the breeders had only 6 interactions with the floaters away from the nest. Nevertheless, the floaters moved elsewhere, and the number dropped from 15 on 18 April to none on 1 May.

The NET area was occupied by territorial adults in three of five breeding seasons (see Figs. 16–19). In 1983, when it was unoccupied, approximately 22 floaters used it in April and all disappeared by 5 May.

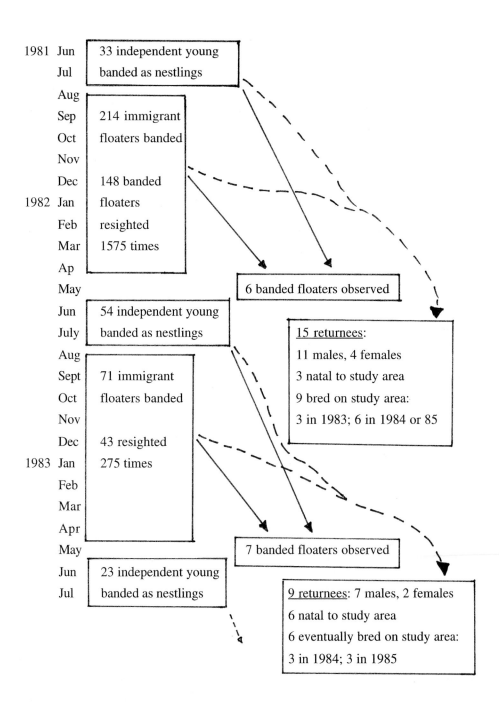

FIGURE 26. Chronology of dispersal and floating showing build-up of floaters during the winter, their disappearance in May, and the number and eventual fate of those that returned in late summer and fall.

The few sightings of floaters during the breeding season, and two contrasting observations described below, make it difficult to generalize about their movement patterns. First, the few floaters seen in May–June 1982 and 1983 were either solitary or in pairs, and used territories as well as the unoccupied interstitial space between territories. This suggests that when the large aggregations broke up, floaters wandered singly or in pairs. Second, seven large flocks (40–50 birds) were observed on the study area between 4–9 May in 1983. In contrast to the loose aggregations during the nonbreeding season, these were cohesive groups and appeared to be traveling long distances. All of the flocks were moving east from hilltop to hilltop. Only one individual in one of these flocks was identified, a floater resighted frequently on the study area. All appeared to be first-year birds. While the timing of flock appearances coincided with the decline in floaters on the study area in general, I observed such large flocks only in 1983. Although purely speculative, these flock movements may result from high breeding success closer to the coast, where habitat is broadly more favorable, including a higher abundance of coast live oak.

Following the 1983 acorn failure, floaters began to arrive on the study area in mid-April 1984, at the same time that many of the breeders returned. Some of these returning breeders became floaters after they failed to regain their territories. In addition, three returning females evicted replacement females on their territories, which then became floaters. By the end of May, most of these floaters had disappeared. Only seven banded floaters were resighted 16 times during this period.

Movements and habitat use during the 1985 breeding season

In fall and winter of 1984, natal juveniles remained on the study area and floaters again immigrated, although in fewer numbers (approximately 40) than in 1981–1982 and 1982–1983. Their unexpected persistence in the spring of 1985 provided an opportunity to acquire data on their behavior during the breeding season.

In the last week in March and the first week of April 1985, 11 floaters were affixed with radio backpacks: three known males, two known females, and three males and three females sexed by discriminant function analysis. All but one were first-year jays. Between 28 March and 12 June, I recorded 270 h of focal animal sampling and radio tracking locations. In addition, 35 "simultaneous" positions of all the tagged jays were taken to examine group movements.

I had expected that by May the jays would move elsewhere, as in previous years. However, only one tagged female disappeared and could not be relocated. Two jays (one male and one female) moved 2 km up Big Creek, off the study area, but remained on local areas throughout May and June.

The other eight tagged jays, and numerous banded and unbanded floaters, remained on the study area. Data on their movements are divided into March–April, when floaters were tolerated by breeders, and the May–June period, when they were not. In March and April, 90% (399 of 445) of all positions for 10 of 11 floaters were on territories (with individual use ranging from 75% to 100%). Despite the early onset of breeding (mean first-egg date was 25 March) and the presence of eggs in nests, floaters still used territories extensively without breeder aggression except near nests.

Figure 27 illustrates composite days (9 sample hours, 57 location points) for three tagged jays (two males and one female) during March and early April 1985. Male (570) was fledged from territory UB in 1984 and tagged and followed in July through September; the other two were immigrants. The tagged jays and other floaters used two main areas, the

BCM/NTANK territories and the EX/LTR territories, with aggregations of approximately 20 and 10 floaters, respectively. It does not appear that breeders confined the floaters to the edges of territories, but they did exclude floaters from nest sites (Fig. 27).

A change in territory LBCM (Fig. 28) had important repercussions for local floater distribution. The LBCM pair consisted of a first-year female and a three-year-old male breeding for the first time. A nest was built, but no eggs were laid. Approximately 15 floaters used the territory extensively. In the first week of May, the pair broke up; the female joined the floaters and the male paired with the COOPERS female, who separated from her new mate. The LBCM territory was abandoned at this time. The vacated LBCM territory became the major center of floater activity in May and June. Other areas with high use included EX/UTR and COOPERS/BUCKM.

In mid-May, seven of the radio-tagged floaters were still on the study area. Three others were 2 km upstream along the same drainage and used the study area occasionally; one was unaccounted for. The telemetry data indicate that even in mid-May, floaters used territories extensively with 45% (412 of 914) positions on occupied territories. If the LBCM territory (occupied by a breeding pair until 5 May) is included as a territorial area, 93% of the positions in May and June were on territories. If LBCM is considered unoccupied, individual floater use of occupied territories varied from 29% to 80%.

Figure 28 shows composite days for four jays (two males and two females) in mid-May. In contrast to winter and early spring locations, floaters used territory boundaries, interstitial areas, and the newly vacated LBCM territory. Yet on several occasions I observed floaters approaching nests with nestlings as close as 20 m, with no response from the breeders. June positions for the 10 radio-tagged jays were similar and by the middle of July the tagged jays were once again tolerated by breeders.

Jay 570, a male fledged on the UB territory the previous spring and radio-tracked the previous July through September (see Fig. 22), remained on or near its natal territory from March through June (Figs. 27a, 28a). Using the boundaries of the 1984 UB territory, 51% of 62 locations in March–April were on its natal territory, but only 10% if the 1985 territory boundaries are used. In May–June, 40% and 3% of the locations were on the 1984 and 1985 territories, respectively. In interactions with its parents, 570 was treated like any other floater, largely ignored on the margin of the territory and rebuffed when near the nest or the breeders. The other UB nestling (also radio-tracked in August and September of 1984, but not in March-June) remained on the EX territory, one km from the UB territory, where it was found throughout April, May, and June of 1985. This jay had no interactions with its parents since the previous spring when, as a juvenile, it left its natal territory.

These data demonstrate that floaters did not use unoccupied habitat, but concentrated their activity on territories. Territory use (Table 7) ranged from an average 98% in August–September, 90% in December–January, 89% in March and April, and 44% in May and June (94% if territory LBCM, deserted in May, is counted as a territory).

Home range of floaters during the 1985 breeding season

Home range estimates are based upon the composite one- or two-day samples from 13–17 May 1985 (five males, two females; Table 8, Fig. 29a), which is the height of the breeding season and, usually, of breeder aggression toward floaters. Individuals used from 3 territories and 2.85 ha (male 447), to portions of 8 territories and 9.73 ha (male 487), with an overall mean of 4.3 territories and 4.9 ha (Table 8). Area use by males and females did not differ. Home range estimates based on radio positions from late April through June are slightly larger (average increase 37%) than those from the one-day samples (Table 8). Thus, during the 1985 breeding season, floater home range was larger than average breeder territory size.

Habitat use by floaters

In four of five breeding seasons, breeders did not tolerate floaters on their territories.

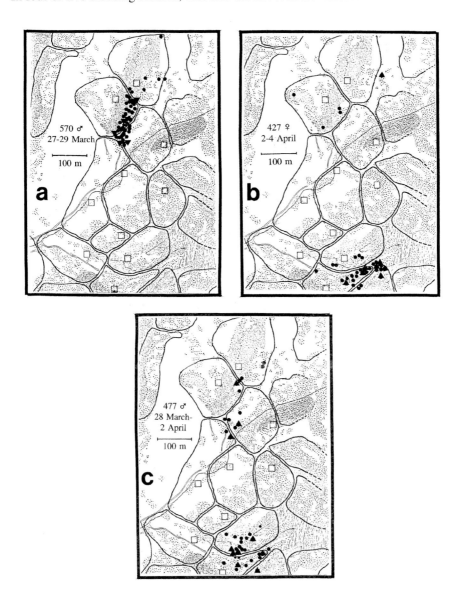

FIGURE 27. Radio-locations and home range of two first-year male floaters and one first-year female floater during late March and early April 1985. Circles indicate one location, triangles ≥2 locations (N = 57 locations), open squares represent nest locations, and solid lines territory boundaries. (a) Male 570 (hatched the previous spring on UB territory and radio tagged as a fledgling (see Fig. 22), (b) Male 477, and (c) Female 427.

TABLE 7. RADIO LOCATION SUMMARIES FROM JULY 1984 THROUGH JUNE 1985

Period	Number of jays	Active locations[a]	Percentage		Out of sight	Off area
			on territory	off territory		
1984						
July	3	422	100%	0%	31	0
August	3	551	98%	2%	45	0
September	2	363	98%	2%	17	0
December	2	430	93%	7%	37	2
1985						
January	1	150	87%	13%	3	9
March	2	93	90%	10%	0	0
April	10	357	88%	12%	12	27
May	9	653	48% (91%)[b]	52% (9%)	31	89
June	6	257	39% (99%)	61% (1%)	4	21

[a] Active points exclude those off study area and unknown locations (jay out of sight). Data points are locations recorded every 10 minutes during 3-hour focal animal samples.

[b] Percentages in parentheses include territory LBCM that was abandoned by the breeders on 5 May.

In 1985, increased tolerance allowed floaters access to occupied territorial space, but mostly near territory edges and away from nest sites. In May and June of 1985 floaters also used the LBCM territory (abandoned in early May) and the margin of the NTANK territory (Figures 27, 28, and 29a); other areas with floaters continued to be occupied by territorial jays.

To assess the quality of the habitat used by floaters, I examined how territorial jays used the area over a several year period. From 1981 through 1985 the reoccurrence of nests on the LBCM and neighboring territories, the contiguous territory boundaries, lack of unoccupied habitat, and the constant occupation of these territories (Fig. 29b) demonstrate that this area, heavily used by floaters in May and June (Fig. 29a), is prime habitat.

Because breeders still could be limiting floaters' access to favorable areas, I collected data on microhabitat use and foraging behavior of floaters and breeders in May–June.

TABLE 8. HOME RANGES OF SEVEN FLOATERS (5 MALES AND 2 FEMALES) DURING MID-MAY 1985 AND THE ENTIRE SAMPLE PERIOD DURING THE BREEDING SEASON

Jay	N of composite sample		Dates	Home range	
	Days	Hours		Size (ha)	Territories overlapped
695 ♀	1	9	16 May	3.07	3
	3	21	8 April–31 May	5.21	4
618 ♂[a]	1	9	13–14 May	3.56	3
	5	45	10 April–14 May	4.55	4
608 ♀	1	9	14–15 May	4.43	4
	4	33	11 April–11 June	4.92	4
487 ♂	1	9	17 May	9.73	8
	3	30	19 April–7 June	14.56	11
570 ♂[a]	1	9	14–15 May	5.53	5
	5	45	27 March–11 June	8.41	6
287 ♂	1	9	15 May	5.38	4
	3	27	15 April–12 June	9.17	6
447 ♂	1	9	15 May	2.85	3
	2	21	28 March–2 June	3.10	4

[a] Sexed by discriminant function analysis (see METHODS).

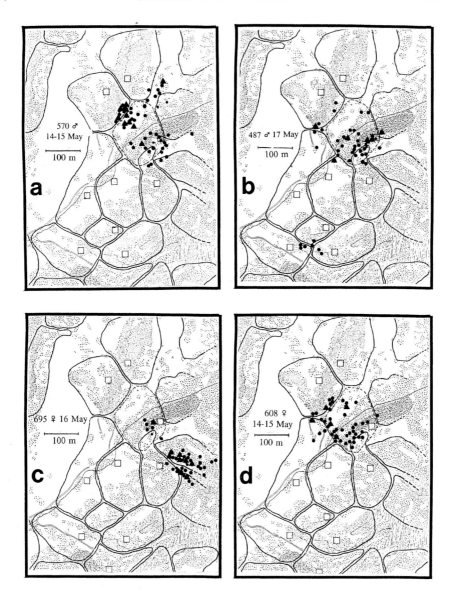

FIGURE 28. Radio-locations and home range of two first-year male floaters and two first-year female floaters during mid-May 1985. Circles indicate one location, triangles ≥ 2 locations (N = 57 locations), open squares represent nest locations, and solid lines territory boundaries. The stippled line indicates the boundary of the LBCM territory that was abandoned on 1 May. (a) Male 570 (hatched the previous spring on UB territory and radio-tagged; see Figs. 22 and 27), (b) Male 487, (c) Female 695, and (d) Female 608.

Data on floaters comes from five radio-tagged individuals that used the LBCM and BUCKM/COOPERS territories; data on breeders comes from the time-budget data collected on four pairs, primarily LBCM, in May 1983. In both samples microhabitat use and foraging style were recorded every 10 min during 3-h focal animal observations. Microhabitat was divided into four categories and foraging method into 10 categories (Fig. 30); no difference existed between breeders and floaters in either case.

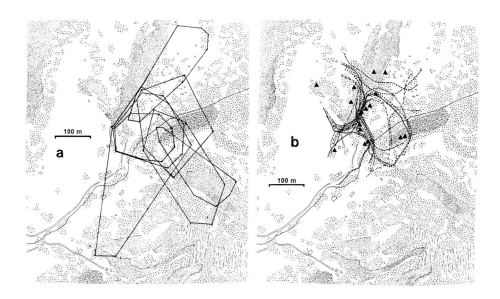

FIGURE 29. Home range of floaters in relation to territories and nest locations. (a) Home range of seven floaters (5 males, two females) in mid-May 1985. Lines represent minimum convex polygons encompassing 57 radio locations on each individual taken during three 3-h watches over a 1- or 2-day period. (b) Territory boundaries in 1981–1985 (each year marked with different line pattern) and nests 1981–1985 (marked with stars) in the LBCM area.

Social Organization of Floaters

Age ratios

In 1981–1982 and 1982–1983, most floaters captured and banded were first-year birds (86.5%, N = 233, and 94%, N = 71, respectively). Estimates from field surveys of floaters in these same years also indicate a ratio of approximately 10:1 in favor of first-year jays; in 1983–1984 no jays floated on the study area. A survey in fall of 1985 revealed approximately 40% of the floaters were adults. Patterns of floater immigration and emigration result in an uneven mixing of the age classes for two reasons. First, a variable but large number of first-year jays immigrated into the study area each year except 1983–1984 when no immigration occurred. Second, nearly all floaters left the study area at the onset of the breeding season and few returned later; 1985 was an exception because of the persistence of floaters through the breeding season. These differing patterns of floater movements may lead to a highly variable age structure of floaters in local areas.

Sex ratio

Twenty-two floaters were sexed as females by their "rattle" calls and the remainder by a discriminant function analysis. In the sample of floaters captured over the entire study period and sexed statistically, 126 of 300 (42%) were classified as males and 174 (58%) as females. Within the aggregation of 17 floaters on the BURNT territory, eight were male, seven female, and two of unknown sex. The sex ratio of floaters at the onset of the breeding season appeared to favor females; of 31 caught in March and April 1982, 11 were male and 20 female; of 54 caught in March and April 1983, 19 were male and 34 female.

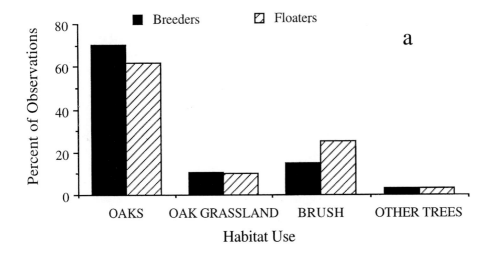

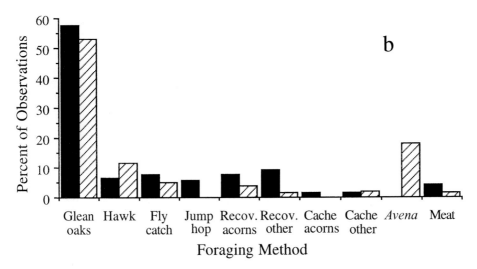

FIGURE 30. Comparison of breeders and floaters in (a) habitat use ($\chi^2 = 0.24$, df = 3, P > 0.90; N = 189 breeders, 224 floaters) and (b) foraging behavior ($\chi^2 = 17.1$, df = 18, P > 0.90; N = 120 breeders, 139 floaters) during the breeding season (5 May–20 May).

Aggregations vs. flocks

I refer to groups of floaters as aggregations rather than flocks, because individuals moved independently of one another. The locations of the radio-tagged floaters in the LBCM area in April and May illustrate the independent movement of individuals. Eight simultaneous locations, taken one hour apart from 0600 to 2000 hours on 7 May, are plotted in Fig. 31. All were located at least once on the LBCM territory (at the center of Fig. 31). Groupings of like symbols would indicate cohesive group movement, but the results show otherwise. Aggregations appeared to form primarily as a result of overlapping home ranges, and thus site serves as a better predictor of a given floater's location than does the presence or absence of other individuals.

Dominance interactions

Linear dominance hierarchies are common in flocks in many birds (Sabine 1959, Fretwell 1969, Smith 1984) including in Florida Scrub-Jay families (Woolfenden and Fitzpatrick 1977). Dominant individuals in flocks may derive at least three advantages compared to less dominant birds: (1) dominants have first access to food (Pulliam 1976); (2) dominants spend more time foraging through decreased time scanning or maintaining alertness for predators (Powell 1974; Caraco 1979a,b; Goldman 1980); and (3) dominants have a greater probability of acquiring a territory or mate in the flock home range (Fretwell 1969, Eden 1987; Smith 1978, 1984). It was therefore surprising that interactions among floaters within aggregations were largely nonaggressive. While interactions were fairly common, most involved supplanting others by moving towards them; chases and aggressive vocalizations, common in breeder-breeder and breeder-floater interactions, were extremely rare. For this reason, data are too limited to determine whether the floaters establish a constant dominance hierarchy. For example, within the BH/DAVIS aggregation, between November 1981 and April 1982, I observed 51 interactions (supplants) between 32 individual floaters where both were identified. Only five jays were seen supplanting more than one other jay, accounting for 22% of the 51 interactions. No reversals were seen, but there were only three cases where the same individuals interacted aggressively on different occasions. However, certain male floaters were clearly more aggressive than others; some of these jays established pseudo-territories in their area of dominance over other floaters.

Floater–floater pairing

By December of most years, <5% of floaters appeared to form pairs as evidenced by courtship feeding and associating closely. Even fewer defended pseudo-territories in April through mid-May. But in 1985, when floaters remained throughout the breeding season, three of 11 radio-tracked floaters formed pairs with untagged birds. None of these pairs built nests and only one pair attempted to defend a territory; the pair was dominant over, but did not exclude, other floaters, but was not dominant over territorial neighbors.

Virtually all breeding vacancies were filled by single jays replacing the mate of a widowed territory holder. Rarely did a floater establish a territory in previously unoccupied areas; in five cases (four by males and one by a female), a jay settled on the new territory and then acquired a mate. Thus, pairing by floaters does not precede or lead directly to territory acquisition.

DISPERSAL DISTANCES

Data from radio-tagged jays and resightings of floaters banded as nestlings indicate that initial dispersal for both sexes can be localized. Natal-to-breeding dispersal distances for 13 males and 6 females that acquired a territory and breeding status on or very near the study area are shown in Fig. 32; females traversed more territories than males (3.2 vs. 1.3). Because these data represent only a small proportion of the jays hatched on the study area that presumably acquired a territory elsewhere, they underestimate average dispersal distances. For example, three individuals banded as first-year floaters in winter were later recorded 32–40 km to the northwest from 5–9 months after banding.

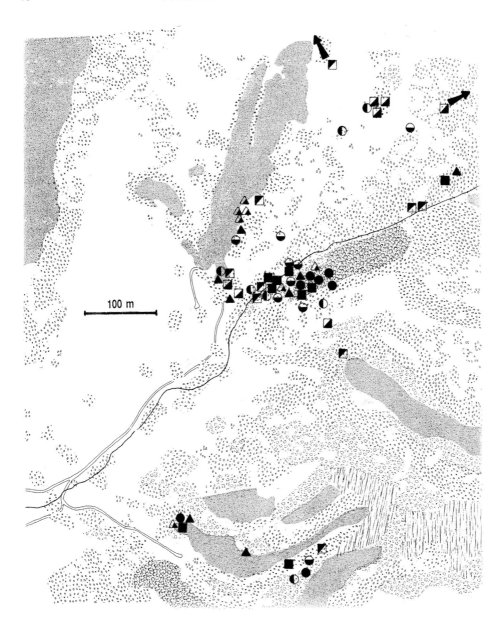

FIGURE 31. Floater association and movements of seven individuals during the breeding season. Eight simultaneous radio-locations were taken one hour apart from 0600 to 2000 hours on 7 May, 1985. The eight different geometric shapes represent the eight simultaneous locations of seven individuals.

REPRODUCTION

Reproductive success depends on many factors. First, a jay must acquire a territory and a mate. Both territory size and quality may influence clutch size (review by Klomp 1970, Högstedt 1980), time of nest initiation (Perrins 1970), and overall reproductive success. Second, fecundity and reproductive success increase with age and past breeding experience in most avian species studied (Klomp 1970, Harvey et al. 1979, Sæther 1990), including the Florida Scrub-Jay (Woolfenden and Fitzpatrick 1984) and the Mexican Jay (Brown 1986). In addition, because reproduction in scrub-jays is a joint effort, attributes of the pair, such as length of pair bond, may enhance breeding success (Woolfenden and Fitzpatrick 1984). Third, annual variation in environmental and ecological conditions may amplify or overwhelm these differences.

In this section, I examine reproductive success of Hastings jays and attempt to unravel the factors that influence an individual's breeding success once it has established a territory.

BREEDING CHRONOLOGY

Nest building typically begins in early March (Fig. 33), although first egg date (FED) varied significantly over the study period (Kruskal-Wallis ANOVA $\chi^2 = 50.9$, df = 4, P < 0.001; Table 9). Jays at Hastings fledged only one brood per year but renested up to two times if earlier nests failed. Over the study period an average of 51% of pairs losing first nests renested. Second broods (renesting after successfully fledging young) have been observed in other populations of Western Scrub-Jays (*A. californica superciliosa*, C. Van Riper, pers. comm.; *A. californica oocleptica*, F. Pitelka, pers. comm.). In Florida Scrub-Jays, 13% of pairs fledging young from first nests attempted to raise second broods (Woolfenden and Fitzpatrick 1984).

Females may begin incubation after the first egg is laid or later, and nestlings hatch synchronously or over several days. The complete nest cycle takes approximately 49

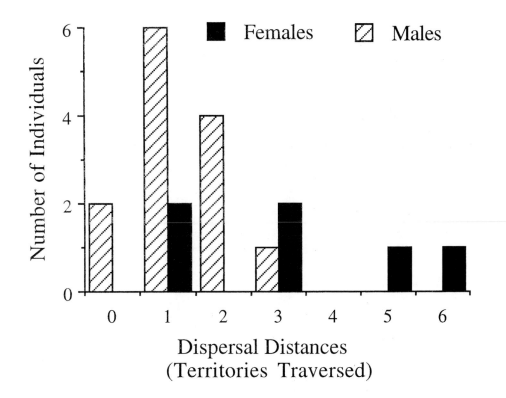

FIGURE 32. Natal-to-breeding dispersal distances within the study area and immediate vicinity. Distance is measured in territories traversed.

days: 3–5 for laying, 19–24 for incubation, and 21–24 from hatching to fledging. Most pairs have nestlings by late April and fledging peaks in late May but extends to mid-July (Fig. 33).

ANNUAL PRODUCTION OF FLEDGLINGS AND INDEPENDENT YOUNG

Tables 10 and 11 summarize the mean annual reproduction variables. Nest failure is high (51% of first nests, 60% of all nests) and renesting increases mean annual production (Table 10) by 25% (fledglings) and 21% (independent young). The proportion of pairs renesting did not vary significantly among years, but ranged from a low of 35% in 1984 (following acorn crop failure) to 58% in 1982 (Chi-square $\chi^2 = 2.3$, df = 4, P > 0.05; Table 9). Overall mean annual production of fledglings was 1.19/pair and varied significantly from 0.62 in 1984 to 1.56 in 1981 (Kruskal-Wallis ANOVA $\chi^2 = 17.5$, df = 4, P = 0.001); independent young averaged 0.88/pair and varied from 0.37 to 1.32 (Kruskal-Wallis ANOVA $\chi^2 = 25.4$, df = 4, P < 0.001; Table 10). Fifty-two percent of pairs monitored from clutch initiation fledged young (43% when all pairs are included; Table 11).

FACTORS INFLUENCING REPRODUCTIVE SUCCESS

Failure to lay eggs

Over five years, the proportion of territorial pairs that laid eggs varied from 96% in 1981 to 62% in 1984 (mean = 81%; Table 11). Only two of 23 first-year female:adult male pairs laid (Table 12), both in 1985. Adult females paired with first-year males laid in 4 of 10 cases. In 1984, 12 of 38 adult pairs did not lay eggs (Table 12), probably because of the poor acorn crop in fall of 1983.

Clutch size

The modal clutch size was 4 (67.9% of 140 complete clutches); three-egg clutches made up 24.3%, and 1, 2, and 5 egg clutches fewer than 8%. Clutch size did not vary among years, with a overall mean of 3.7 and annual range of 3.5 to 3.8 (Table 11). The modal clutch size was the most productive in four of five years, but three-egg clutches produced more fledglings in 1983.

Survival of eggs, nestlings, and fledglings

Data on survival (Table 13) are based on 761 eggs and 460 nestlings in 208 nests. The samples include nests where clutch size (67) and brood size (20) were not determined (see METHODS); in these cases the mean clutch size (3.7) or brood size (3.0) was assumed. Hatching success ranged from 53% in 1984 to 70% in 1985 (mean = 61%) and

TABLE 9. FIRST EGG DATE (MEAN ± SD) AND THE PERCENTAGE OF PAIRS RENESTING

Year	Number of pairs	First egg date	Range	Pairs renesting
1981	25	7 April ± 10	29 March–22 April	55% (6/11)
1982	51	7 April ± 10	20 March–27 April	58% (11/19)
1983	52	7 April ± 7	28 March–21 April	48% (14/29)
1984	42	20 April ± 11	7 April–7 May	35% (6/17)
1985	45	25 March ± 7	12 March–10 April	57% (8/14)
Overall	215	7 April ± 8	12 March–7 May	51%

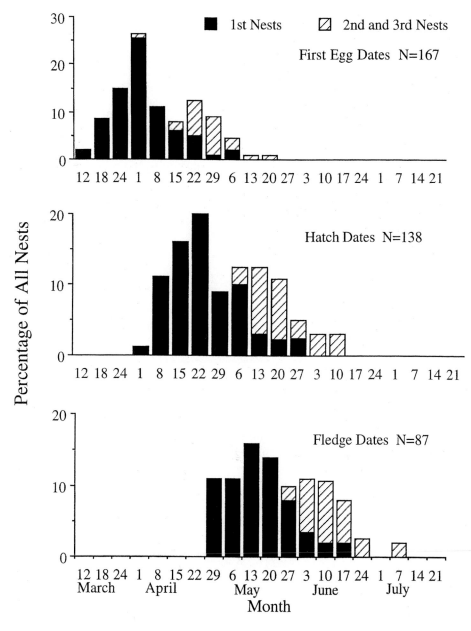

FIGURE 33. Nesting chronology of Hastings scrub-jays, 1981–1985.

fledging success from 18–40% (mean = 30%). Losses from fledging to one month post-fledging averaged 27%, and ranged from 14% to 44%. Years with low fledging success also showed the lowest fledgling survival (R_s = 0.99, P < 0.05).

Key-factor analysis

Key-factor analysis (Varley and Gradwell 1960) can be used to determine which factor

TABLE 10. ANNUAL PRODUCTION (MEAN ± SD) OF FLEDGLINGS AND INDEPENDENT YOUNG (NUMBER OF PAIRS IN PARENTHESES)

	First nests only		All nests	
Year	Fledge	Independent[a]	Fledge	Independent
1981	1.21 ± 1.4	1.08 ± 1.2	1.52 ± 1.5	1.32 ± 1.3
	(25)	(25)	(25)	(25)
1982	1.08± 1.5	0.76 ± 1.1	1.56 ± 1.6	1.08 ± 1.3
	(51)	(51)	(50)	(50)
1983	0.58 ± 1.1	0.37 ± 0.9	0.79 ± 1.2	0.45 ± 0.9
	(52)	(52)	(52)	(51)
1984	0.50 ± 1.6	0.32 ± 0.9	0.62 ± 1.2	0.37 ± 1.0
	(42)	(41)	(42)	(41)
1985	1.16 ± 1.5	0.96 ±1.3	1.44 ± 1.5	1.18 ± 1.3
	(45)	(45)	(45)	(45)
Pooled	0.87 ± 1.4	0.66 ± 1.1	1.16 ± 1.5	0.84 ± 1.2
Means	0.91 ± 0.3	0.70 ± 0.3	1.19 ± 0.4	0.88 ± 0.4
	(215)	(214)	(214)	(212)

[a] Young counted as independent at 4 weeks after fledging.

was primarily responsible for variation in reproductive success. First, maximum potential egg production is estimated. Then, actual egg production is measured and subsequent survivorship is followed. Thus, comparisons are between potential and actual production. This allows less tangible factors such as failure to lay eggs, failure to renest, etc., to be considered. The data are converted to logarithms, and total mortality is obtained by summing the individual mortality events ($k_1 + k_2 + ... + k_n = k_{total}$). Thus, k_{total} is the difference between potential and actual production. When the k values are plotted against time, the k-factor that is largest and parallels k_{total} is designated the key factor responsible for the variability. This need not always be the largest portion of annual mortality; for example, in Common Woodpigeons (*Columba palumbus*), 80% of all eggs were taken by predators, but this contributed little to the observed fluctuations in annual mortality (Murton and Westwood 1977).

TABLE 11. ANNUAL VARIATION IN REPRODUCTIVE VARIABLES

		Percent	Clutch	% of eggs		% of hatched	% fledged to	Breeding success	
Year	N	breeding	size	Hatched	Fledged	eggs fledged[a]	independence	Breeding	All
1981	25	96%	3.5±1.0	64.2%	32.0%	50%	87%	67.0%	64.0%
	(6/11)	(50/78)	(25/50)	(33/38)	(16/24)	(16/25)			
1982	51	82%	3.8±0.5	59.6%	40.4%	68%	69%	61.0%	52.9%
	(11/19)	(109/183)	(74/109)	(54/78)	(27/44)	(27/51)			
1983	52	85%	3.7±0.7	56.3%	19.7%	35%	59%	36.0%	30.8%
	(14/29)	(117/208)	(4l/117)	(23/39)	(16/44)	(16/52)			
1984	42	62%	3.8±0.4	53.0%	18.8%	35%	63%	27.0%	16.7%
	(6/17)	(62/117)	(22/62)	(15/24)	(7/26)	(7/42)			
1985	45	84%	3.7±0.6	69.7%	37.1%	53%	82%	66.0%	55.6%
	(8/14)	(122/175)	(65/122)	(53/65)	(24/38)	(24/45)			
Mean	216	81%	3.7	60.6%	29.6%	48%	72%	52.0%	43.2%
		$\chi^2 = 15.8$	$\chi^2 = 2.4$	$\chi^2 = 11$	$\chi^2 = 31$	$\chi^2 = 30$	$\chi^2 = 11.8$	$\chi^2 = 16.8$	$\chi^2 = 24.6$
		P = 0.003	P = 0.66	P = 0.03	P < 0.001	P < 0.001	P < 0.01	P = 0.002	P < 0.001

Note: Tests for differences among years in reproductive variables by χ^2 contingency except clutch size and mean fledged by Kruskal-Wallis ANOVA.

[a] Clutch size undetermined in 62 cases and brood size in 20; mean clutch size (3.7 eggs) and brood size (3.0 chicks) were assumed.

TABLE 12. Age composition of pairs and number initiating breeding

| Year | Composition | | Number of pairs | | |
	Male	Female	Total	Followed	Breeding
1981	Adult	Adult	29	24	24 (100%)
	1st yr	Adult	0	—	—
	Adult	1st yr	1	1	0
1982	Adult	Adult	40	40	40 (100%)
	1st yr	Adult	6	6	3 (50%)
	Adult	1st yr	5	5	0
1983	Adult	Adult	46	44	44 (100%)
	1st yr	Adult	2	2	0
	Adult	1st yr	6	6	0 (100%)
1984	Adult	Adult	39	38	26 (68%)
	1st yr	Adult	0	—	—
	Adult	1st yr	4	4	0
1985	Adult	Adult	35	35	35 (100%)
	1st yr	Adult	2	2	1 (50%)
	Adult	1st yr	7	7	2 (29%)
	1st yr	1st yr	1	1	0
Total	Adult	Adult	188	181	171 (94%)
	1st yr	Adult	10	10	4 (40%)
	Adult	1st yr	23	23	2 (9%)
	1st yr	1st yr	1	1	0
Grand total			223	215	177 (82%)

I considered the following variables (Table 11):

1. *Maximum potential egg production*: the modal clutch size, four, was taken as the maximum, as five egg clutches comprised only 5% of all clutches. Each year many first nests fail. I therefore added the corresponding number of eggs to potential egg production, assuming that all of these pairs could lay replacement clutches. Because only 51% of pairs renested, this overestimates potential egg production but does not effect the results of the analysis.

2. *"Mortality" events*: (a) k_1: failure to lay eggs; (b) k_2: failure to lay four eggs in clutch; (c) k_3: failure to renest; (d) k_4: egg loss; (e) k_5: nestling loss; (f) k_6: fledgling loss (to one month).

The results are plotted in Fig. 34. Nestling mortality (k_5) contributes greatest to k_{total} and parallels it most closely. However, several other factors influence k_{total}. In 1984 all factors increased except modal clutch size (k_2), and failure to lay (k_1) jumped appreciably; 1984 was the only year some adult-adult pairs failed to lay.

Causes of nest and fledgling mortality

Although losses of nestlings contributed most to annual fluctuations in reproductive output, egg and fledgling losses were also considerable. Here I assume, first, that losses of entire clutches and broods, not due to breeder death or abandonment, were due to predators; usually physical evidence confirmed this. Second, nestlings that disappeared from continuing broods were counted as having starved to death; this ignores partial brood predation (no cases detected) and also disease and parasites (probably minimal). For broods of one, no cause was assigned.

Of the 208 nests, 84 (40.4%) fledged young (Table 13). Predation accounted for most

TABLE 13. FATE OF EGGS, FLEDGLINGS, AND NESTS

	Individuals			Nests		
	N	% individuals	% loss	N	% nests	% loss
Eggs and nests	761	100%		208	100%	
losses due to:						
Hatching failure	39	5.1%	12.0%	0		
Desertion	3	0.4%	1.0%	1	0.5%	1.4%
Breeder death	20	2.6%	6.7%	6	2.9%	8.2%
Predation	239	31.4%	79.4%	66	31.7%	90.4%
Total lost before hatching	301	39.5%	100%	73	35.1%	100%
Nestlings and nests	460	100%		135	100%	
losses due to:						
Breeder death	15	3.3%	6.4%	4	3.0%	7.8%
Starvation	79	17.2%	33.9%	—[a]	—[a]	—[a]
Predation	132	28.7%	56.7%	41	30.4%	80.4%
Ambiguous	7	1.5%	3.0%	6	4.4%	11.8%
Total lost after hatching	233	50.7%	100%	51	37.8%	100%
Survivorship	227	29.8%	(eggs)	84	40.4%	
		49.3%	(nestlings)		62.2%	

[a] All losses of entire broods assumed to be caused by predation.

losses during the egg and nestling stages, abandonment and breeder death less than 10%, and starvation 17.2%.

Yearly variation in predation and starvation

Predation on eggs averaged 31.7% but varied significantly over the five years, as did predation on nestlings (mean = 30.6%; Table 14). The mean percentage of nestlings starving (16.3%) was not statistically different among years.

ECOLOGICAL AND ENVIRONMENTAL EFFECTS

Weather

For scrub-jays at Hastings, I found no significant correlations between weather variables (mean annual, winter, and spring rainfall; mean, mean minimum, and mean maximum winter and spring temperatures) and reproductive variables (including FED and overall mean annual reproductive success). Nor did I find any significant correlations between weather and the annual relative abundance of the diet fed to nestlings (e.g., flying insects from the yellow-pan samples or ground-dwelling insects from the grassland sweep samples) or acorn crops (from surveys of 250 oaks; Carmen et al. 1987).

Food and reproduction

Correlations among four reproductive variables and the relative abundance of several food types are presented in Table 15. Total flying insect abundance was positively correlated with FED (i.e., higher insect abundance coincided with later FED). This is surprising and counterintuitive because jays usually initiate breeding before adult insects become abundant, and early onset of breeding is expected to be correlated with higher insect abundance. I was unable to measure the relative abundance of lepidopteran larvae on oak leaves, which are the main prey of jays early in the spring and more likely to influences reproductive activity.

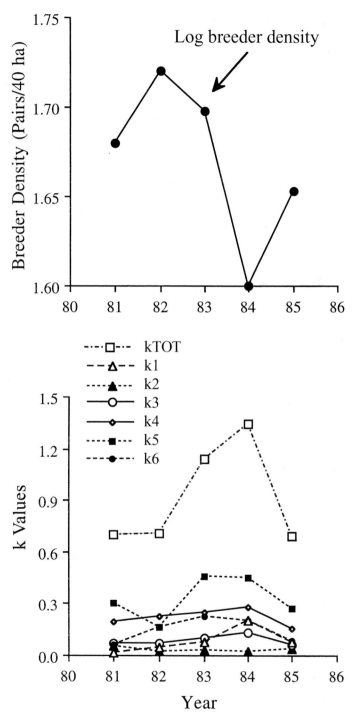

FIGURE 34. Log of breeder density (pairs/40 ha) and k-values 1981–1985 (see text for explanation of key-factor analysis). k1: failure to lay eggs; k2: failure to lay four eggs in clutch; k3: failure to renest; k4: egg loss; k5: nestling loss; k6: fledgling loss.

TABLE 14. ANNUAL PREDATION AND STARVATION RATES OF EGGS, NESTLINGS, AND NESTS

	Predation on				Starvation of
Year	Eggs	Nestlings	E+N combined	Nests	nestlings
1981	29.6%	38.0%	51%	50%	12.0%
	(21/78)	(19/50)	(40/78)	(12/24)	(6/50)
1982	32.8%	10.1%	39%	39%	16.5%
	(60/183)	(11/109)	(71/183)	(20/51)	(18/109)
1983	37.0%	35.9%	57%	64%	20.5%
	(77/208)	(42/117)	(119/208)	(36/56)	(24/117)
1984	38.5%	40.3%	60%	63%	14.5%
	(45/117)	(25/62)	(70/117)	(19/30)	(9/62)
1985	20.6%	28.7%	41%	42%	18.0%
	(36/175)	(35/122)	(71/175)	(20/47)	(22/122)
Mean	31.7%	30.6%	50%	52%	16.3%
	$\chi^2 = 16$	$\chi^2 = 27$	$\chi^2 = 24$	$\chi^2 = 10$	$\chi^2 = 2.3$
	P = 0.003	P = 0.001	P < 0.001	P = 0.03	P > 0.05

Note: Statistical tests of differences in predation and starvation losses among years by chi-square contingency.

Both total acorn abundance and the abundance of *Q. agrifolia* acorns were correlated with standardized FED and overall breeding success (Table 15). When acorns, particularly those of *Q. agrifolia*, were abundant, scrub-jays bred earlier and were more successful.

To test whether acorn availability enhances reproductive success, I supplied four pairs of jays with acorns during the crop failure of 1983–1984. Each week, from late December through March, I placed 200 acorns on an elevated feeding platform at the center of each territory. The jays in all cases responded quickly and stored the acorns within 30 min. The fed pairs all laid eggs (compared to 22 of 34 unfed pairs) and laid an average of 15 days earlier than the average for the unfed pairs (see discussion of effect of acorn supplementation on time-budgets of jays). Schoech (1996) found that Florida Scrub-Jays fed supplemental dog food from January to clutch completion laid their clutches an average 16 days earlier than nonsupplemented groups.

Timing

At Hastings, while neither clutch size nor production from first nests alone is correlated with standardized FED, the number of independent young from first nests, and total fledged and independent young from all nest attempts, was greater for early nesting pairs

TABLE 15. SPEARMAN RANK CORRELATIONS OF MEAN ANNUAL REPRODUCTION VARIABLES WITH ANNUAL ACORN AND INSECT ABUNDANCE (N = 5 YEARS)

Mean	Yellow-pan insects	Sweep-net insects	Total acorns	*Q. agrifolia* acorns only
FED[a]	0.94**	0.20	–0.76*	–1.00***
Fledged	–0.21	–0.16	0.60	0.52
Independent	–0.32	0.34	0.17	0.45
Percent successful	–0.54	0.45	0.75*	0.85**

[a] First egg date, standardized so that the earliest egg each year falls on the same date.
*0.1 > P > 0.05
**0.05 > P > 0.01
***0.01 > P > 0.001

(Spearman rank test, all P < 0.01). To examine what factors contribute to higher success of jays initiating breeding early in the spring, unstandardized FED was divided into three categories: early (prior to 1 April), middle (1 April to 12 April), and late (past 12 April). The middle category's midpoint is 6 April, the overall mean FED for the population. The results of this analysis indicate that the benefits of early nesting occur in two ways. First, early nesters had a higher probability of renesting; 60%, 53% and 6% for early-, middle-, and late-nesters, respectively (R×C test, P < 0.001). Second, early nesters experienced lower fledgling losses; 14%, 37%, and 33% for early-, middle-, and late-nesters, respectively (R×C test, P < 0.001).

The benefits of early nesting are not likely to end at independence. In several studies, early-fledging individuals have greater competitive ability or higher status leading to an improved probability of obtaining a territory and breeding (e.g. Eurasian Magpies [Eden 1987]; Black-capped Chickadees, *Poecile atricapillus* [Glase 1973]; Eurasian Nuthatches, *Sitta europaea* [Matthysen 1987]; and Song Sparrows [Arcese and Smith 1985]).

Breeder density

Breeder density varied from 9.2–12.2 pairs/40 ha (Table 3); the correlation with annual fledgling production was not significant. Highest fledgling production came in 1982, the year of highest breeder density, and the lowest in 1984 with the lowest breeder density.

Territory quality

No discernable relationship existed between territory quality and mean annual fledgling production; 1.3, 1.1, and 0.9 fledglings per territory for Types 1 through Type 3, respectively (Kruskal-Wallis ANOVA $\chi^2 = 1.3$, df = 2, P = 0.37). Although the trend is in the expected direction, factors such as high rates of nest loss and differences in parental quality, particularly those associated with age effects, may obscure the effect of territory quality on measured reproductive success.

EFFECTS OF AGE AND EXPERIENCE

Age of breeders

Age is the most important influence on reproductive success (Table 16). Adult pairs comprised the vast majority of all pairs and were responsible for nearly all successful reproduction (98% of 253 fledglings). Of 23 adult male:first-year female pairs on true territories, only two pairs laid and hatched young and only one fledged young. All 23 adult male:first-year female pairs successfully defended territories, built nests, and in all other respects appeared to be stable, bonded pairs. An additional four adult male:first-year female pairs defended pseudo-territories. Of 10 first-year male:adult-female pairs, four laid eggs, two hatched young, but none fledged young. Also, none of these pairs established pseudo-territories. Only one first-year pair defended a territory throughout the breeding season; no eggs were laid.

To determine whether age beyond the first year affects reproduction, I compared the reproductive output of jays of one sex from 2 to ≥ 5 year-old paired with jays of the other sex two years or older; hence, the age of the mate of a jay of a given age could vary from two years to the potential longevity in the population (the oldest known breeder, a male, was 11 years old in 1987). Although the age of both members of a pair is important, there were few pairs where the exact age of both individuals was known.

Female age was significantly correlated with standardized FED, clutch size, total fledged, and total independent young (Table 17). This was true also of FED with age of male, and approaches significance with total fledged ($P = 0.06$) and independent young ($P = 0.08$; Table 17). These relationships are broken down by age class in Table 18 and Figure 35, and reveal a significant decrease in FED and a significant increase in fledglings and independent young per pair for females and males through age four (when first-year birds are included, all variables show a significant increase with age). Most of these variables varied significantly among years, but the relationships between age and reproduction also hold within a single year (1985), the year with the most complete data (Fig. 35). However, because most of the data for the older age classes are from 1985 (a good production year), the values may slightly overestimate average reproductive output for the older age classes.

Duration of pair bond

FED and years together as a pair shows a significant negative correlation ($R_s = -0.36$, $P < 0.01$; Table 17); the longer the pair remained intact, the earlier it nested. Jays with enduring pair bonds nested an average 10 days earlier than recently paired jays.

Prior breeding experience

In comparisons between novice and experienced pairs older than one year, neither FED, number fledged, and number independent were statistically significant, despite nearly twice the fledgling output of experienced pairs (Table 19).

SURVIVORSHIP

Patterns of age- and sex-specific survival affect population structure (Caughley 1977), mating systems (Murray 1984), social organization (Woolfenden and Fitzpatrick 1984), and overall fitness, through their influence on life-time reproductive success (Koenig and Mumme 1987, van Balen et al. 1987, Fitzpatrick and Woolfenden 1988, Fitzpatrick et al. 1989). Newly independent young in most cooperatively breeding species face the options of independent breeding or delayed dispersal (and helping); in noncooperative species, the options are independent breeding or floating. Survivorship plays a key role in determining the relative benefits of these options. Increased survivorship of helpers on their natal territories and their assisted parents are hypothesized to be important factors favoring delayed dispersal and cooperative breeding (Brown 1974, Emlen 1982, Koenig and Pitelka 1981, Woolfenden and Fitzpatrick 1984; Arnold and Owens 1998, 1999). In

TABLE 16. PERCENTAGE OF TERRITORIAL PAIRS BY AGE COMPOSITION THAT LAID EGGS, BREEDING SUCCESS, AND MEAN NUMBER FLEDGED

Age composition	Number of pairs	% breeding	% breeding success	Mean number fledged	Total number fledged
Both first-year	1	0%	0%	0	0
Adult ♂: first-year ♀	23	8.7%	4.3%	0.1	2
First-year ♂: adult ♀	10	40.0%	10.0%	0.3	3
Both adult	181	94.0%	60.0%	1.4	248

TABLE 17. SPEARMAN RANK CORRELATIONS OF FOUR REPRODUCTIVE VARIABLES WITH AGE OF MALE (2 TO 5+ YEARS), AGE OF FEMALE (2 TO 5+ YEARS), AND YEARS TOGETHER AS A PAIR (0 TO 2) (N IN PARENTHESES)

	Age of male	Age of female	Years together
FED[a]	−0.45	−0.48	−0.36
	(44)	(32)	(58)
	P = 0.009	P = 0.002	P = 0.01
Clutch	0.21	0.44	0.04
	(33)	(26)	(48)
	NS[b]	P = 0.02	NS
Fledge	0.24	0.41	0.12
	(60)	(46)	(83)
	P = 0.06	P = 0.005	NS
Independent young	0.23	0.32	0.13
	(60)	(46)	(83)
	P = 0.08	P = 0.03	NS

[a] First egg date standardized so that the first egg each year falls on the same date.
[b] $P > 0.10$.

addition, survivorship of breeders may largely determine how many breeding vacancies open, and the survivorship of floaters (and helpers) determines the intensity of competition for these vacancies.

Here I examine survivorship of both territorial breeders and nonterritorial floaters and calculate sex- and age-specific survival rates based on population averages over a five-year study period. The resulting life table allows calculation of other key demographic parameters that are important in evaluating the costs and benefits of early dispersal and floating.

TABLE 18. EFFECTS OF BREEDER AGE ON REPRODUCTION (MEAN ± SD) (N IN PARENTHESES)

	Age (yr)					P[a]
	1	2	3	4	5+	
FED[b]						
Female	–	7 Ap ± 14	12 Ap ± 17	21 Mr ± 7	24 Mr ± 7	$\chi^2 = 11.4$
	(0)	(8)	(7)	(6)	(11)	P = 0.001
Male	8 Ap ± 13	20 Ap ± 15	10 Ap ± 14	28 Mr ± 10	1 Ap ± 13	$X^2 = 7.64$
	(2)	(4)	(8)	(4)	(28)	P = 0.05
Clutch size						
Female	–	3.1 ± 1.1	3.6 ± 0.5	3.5 ± 0.6	4.0 ± 0.5	$\chi^2 = 4.23$
	(8)	(7)	(6)	(11)	NS	
Male	3.0 ± 0	2.5 ± 2.1	3.7 ± 0.5	3.5 ± 0.6	3.7 ± 0.8	$\chi^2 = 5.01$
	(2)	(2)	(7)	(4)	(21)	NS
Fledglings						
Female	0.08 ± 0.4	0.7 ± 1.3	1.1 ± 1.5	2.4 ± 1.1	2.2 ± 1.8	$\chi^2 = 8.7$
	(24)	(1 5)	(9)	(8)	(14)	P = 0.03
Male	0.3 ± 1.0	0.6 ± 1.5	0.8 ± 1.2	1.7 ± 1.3	1.6 ± 1.6	$\chi^2 = 3.1$
	(9)	(7)	(10)	(7)	(36)	NS
Independent young						
Female	0.04 ± 0.2	0.6 ± 1.1	1.1 ± 1.5	2.0 ± 1.1	1.7 ± 1.6	$\chi^2 = 6.7$
	(24)	(15)	(9)	(8)	(14)	P = 0.08
Male	0.3 ± 1.0	0.4 ± 1.1	0.3 ± 0.5	1.1 ± 1.1	1.2 ± 1.4	$\chi^2 = 2.2$
	(9)	(7)	(10)	(7)	(36)	NS

[a] Kruskal-Wallis tests of differences among ages classes 2–5; if age class 1 is included all comparisons are significant. NS denotes $P > 0.10$.
[b] FED = first egg date. Ap=April, Mr=March.

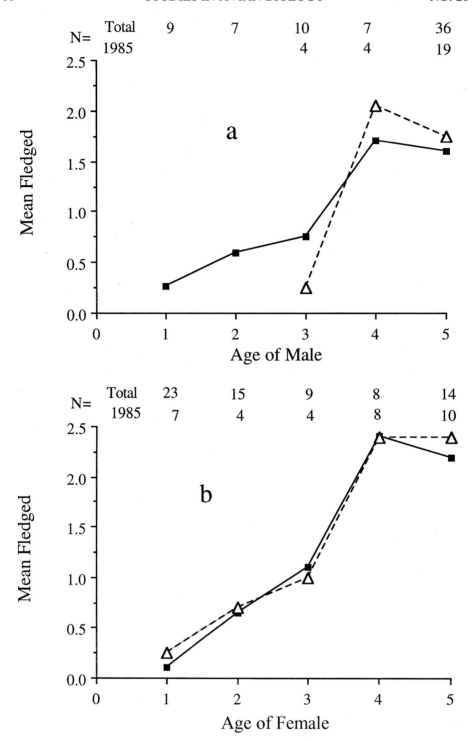

FIGURE 35. Age-specific fledgling production of breeding males (a) and females (b). Pooled data from all years, and for 1985 only, are plotted. Sample sizes for each year are plotted across the top.

TABLE 19. EFFECT OF PAST BREEDING EXPERIENCE ON REPRODUCTION (PAIRS THAT INCLUDED A FIRST-YEAR JAY ARE EXCLUDED) (NUMBER OF NESTS IN PARENTHESES)

	No prior experience	Experienced	P[a]
First egg date	9 April ± 12	3 April ± 12	Z = 1.25
	(6)	(52)	P = 0.21
Young fledged	0.73 ± 1.1	1.39 ± 1.6	Z = −1.13
	(11)	(70)	P = 0.26
Independent young	0.6 ± 0.9	1.01 ± 1.3	Z = −0.82
	(10)	(70)	P = 0.41

[a] Mann-Whitney U-tests for differences in variables between experienced and inexperienced breeders.

SURVIVORSHIP OF BREEDERS

Assumptions

Once a scrub-jay acquires a territory and breeding status, it typically retains both until death. Although it is usually not possible to separate deaths from emigration, several lines of evidence indicate that death was responsible for virtually all breeder disappearance on the study area.

Scrub-jays at Hastings rarely leave their territories. As no floater was ever seen to dominate a breeder, it is unlikely that breeders were ever evicted by floaters. Excluding 1983–1984 (the year of the acorn crop failure), only one individual assumed dead later returned to its territory. In that case, neither the male nor female was seen on their territory between October and February, when the male returned with a first-year female. In contrast, between August 1983 and February 1984, 59 of 103 banded breeders disappeared; 38 returned later, most in March and April.

Typically, jays that lost a mate remained on their own territory and acquired a new mate from the pool of floaters. However, in several instances, a known breeder paired with the resident on a different territory. This presents two lines of possible error in calculating survivorship rates. First, it was not always clear whether these jays separated from their mates or their mates had died. I classified them as separations if the bird was later seen as a floater (i.e., adults with breeding experience can become floaters); however, the probability of observing such individuals is low and the calculations of survivorship may be artificially low. However, separations were relatively rare.

Second, individuals that move away from the study area may be undetected. However, data on breeder movements on the study area indicate that they are of very limited distance. On surveys surrounding the study area, only one former breeder was found—a male that had disappeared during the acorn crop failure. I therefore conclude that I detected nearly all permanent moves of breeders off their original territories.

ANNUAL SURVIVORSHIP

Annual survivorship was calculated from 1 April to 31 March each year, and data from 74 banded males and 72 banded females (292 breeder-years) were analyzed. Survival was calculated by comparing the number of jays at risk during the period to the number alive at the end of the period. I include two samples derived slightly differently: (1) an entire year sample that includes only those individuals already banded at the beginning of the period (1 April); and (2) a "partial" year sample that includes the above jays plus those banded after 1 April of a given year. In the latter sample, if the jays banded after 1

April survived, the fraction of the year as a banded breeder is added to the calculation of survivorship. Using the partial year sample increases the sample sizes, especially for the early years of the study when comparatively few breeders were color-banded.

Annual variation in survivorship of breeders (all ages pooled) is presented in Table 20. Overall male survivorship (partial year sample) ranged between 71.5% and 89.7% with a four-year mean of 83.4%. Female survivorship was lower in every year, but not statistically different from that of males, ranging from 62.7% to 84.5% and averaging 77.9%.

Male and female survivorships were correlated ($R_s = 0.96$, N = 5) and were not statistically different among years. Survivorship was similar in all years except 1983–1984, and territorial jays that disappeared after August 1983 and had not returned by late April 1984 were considered dead as a result of the crop failure. In all, an estimated 30 out of 103 banded jays (the fall 1983 study population) died in this year, 45% of deaths during the 5-year study. The crop failure affected males and females equally, with 16 female and 14 male deaths, constituting 33% and 29% of the banded territorial jays in fall 1983.

Seasonal patterns

To analyze seasonal patterns of breeder mortality, I divided the year into the breeding season (March–June), late summer dry period and molt (July–October), and winter (November–February). Mortality did not vary significantly by season either for males (N = 32) or females (N = 35; Fig. 36a) or for both sexes combined. Although the proportion of females dying during the breeding season is twice that of males, the differences are not statistically significant, in my view because of small sample sizes. Excluding deaths attributable to the acorn crop failure results in similar distributions of seasonal and gender mortality (Fig. 36b).

TABLE 20. ANNUAL SURVIVORSHIP OF BREEDERS

Year		Males	Females
1981–1982			
	Entire years[a]	85.7% (14)[c]	84.0% (11)
	Partial years[b]	89.7% (25)	84.5% (18)
1982–1983			
	Entire years	88.4% (43)	79.4% (34)
	Partial years	89.7% (52)	83.3% (47)
1983–1984			
	Entire years	70.4% (54)	61.4% (44)
	Partial years	71.5% (59)	62.7% (51)
1984–1985			
	Entire years	82.4% (51)	81.0% (42)
	Partial years	82.6% (53)	81.3% (44)
Overall (mean of annual values)			
	Entire years	81.7% (162)	76.5% (131)
	Partial years	83.4% (189)	77.9% (160)

Year % mortality: $G = 10.3$, df = 3, $0.025 > P > 0.01$
Sex % mortality: $G = 2.0$, df = 3, $P > 0.10$

[a] Entire years include only scrub-jays banded by 1 April.
[b] Partial years include scrub-jays banded by 1 April and those banded before the next 1 April. For scrub-jays banded after 1 April, if the scrub-jay died during the year it was counted as dead; if it lived, the proportion of the year since banding was added into the calculation of survivorship.
[c] Total number of scrub-jays at risk during the year.

Age-specific survivorship of breeders

Survivorship calculated on a yearly basis as above, where all individuals are lumped, ignores differences in age-specific survivorship. On the other hand, lumping all years to calculate age-specific mortality ignores the effects of annual variation. Ideally, age-specific mortality should be compared within years among cohorts (e.g., Sherman and Morton 1984, Gibbs and Grant 1987), but this requires large sample sizes. I therefore calculated age-specific survivorship as averages for same-age jays from different cohorts.

Age-specific survivorship schedules for breeders (Table 21) suggested that survivorship was not greatly affected by age of adults. One complication is the relatively few sample years and the large drop in survivorship during the acorn crop failure, which appeared to affect breeders irrespective of age. Adult mortality rate in birds is often assumed to be age-constant (but see Caughley 1977) and some long-term studies support the concept (e.g., Island Scrub-Jays [Atwood et al. 1990], Acorn Woodpeckers [Koenig and Mumme 1987]); others do not (Loery et al. 1987). In the Florida Scrub-Jay, Fitzpatrick and Woolfenden (1988) found constant survivorship of breeders through age 11 followed by a sharp decrease, suggesting senescent mortality.

Woolfenden and Fitzpatrick (1984) and Koenig and Mumme (1987) examined senescent mortality by comparing survivorship of known vs. unknown aged breeders. In this study, for a breeder's age to be known I had to band it when no more than 15 months old at which time it enters the first complete molt. Because the study includes only four years of survivorship, the known-age sample excludes jays older than five. If survivorship decreases with age, the known-age sample (N = 44) should show higher survivorship than the unknown age sample (N = 102); however, no difference was found (Lee-Desu survivorship statistic D = 0.03, P = 0.8).

I also compared the survivorship of jays that began breeding as first-year birds (N = 31) with those waiting until two or older (N = 27). Survivorship over one year (e.g., from one to two for first-year birds and from two to three for a two-year old) is not statistically different for the two groups (χ^2 = 2.0, P = 0.15), although older first-time breeder survivorship averaged 89% vs. 74% for first-year breeders. Calculated over a several-year period, jays that bred as yearlings experienced higher mortality (annual average = 18.9%) than jays waiting until two or three (annual average 11.2%; Lee-Desu survivorship statistic, D = 3.6, P = 0.058). Of course, this may be due to lower survivorship of first-year birds rather than any effect from a delay in breeding. The definitive comparison, which I am unable to make, would be between first-year territorial jays and first-year nonbreeding floaters, an important but elusive parameter in weighing the costs and benefits of delayed vs. early dispersal.

TABLE 21. AGE SPECIFIC SURVIVORSHIP OF KNOWN AGE MALE AND FEMALE BREEDERS FROM AGE 1 TO ≥ 5 YR

	Males				Females		
Age	Number at risk	Number survived	% survival	Age	Number at risk	Number survived	% survival
1	9	8	89	1	18	15	83
2	14	11	79	2	13	10	77
3	9	8	89	3	8	7	87
4	4	3	75	4	—	—	—
≥ 5	50	40	80	≥ 5	28	20	72

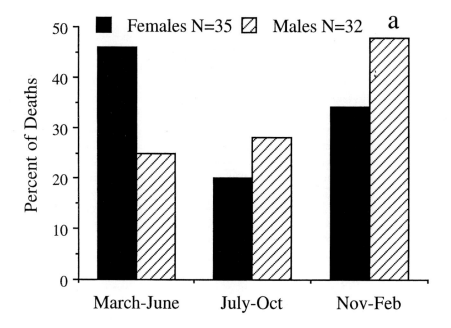

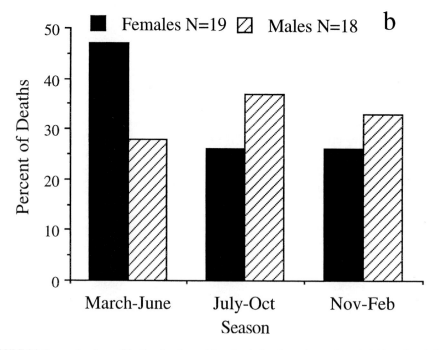

FIGURE 36. Seasonal pattern of deaths of males and females during the entire study period (a), and excluding deaths during the acorn crop failure (b).

Ignoring the possible decreased survivorship of jays acquiring a territory as yearlings, composite survivorship curves (Fig. 37) using all banded breeders, show an expected survivorship of 83% for males and 79% for females.

LIFE TABLES AND SURVIVORSHIP OF NONBREEDERS

Determining the survivorship of juveniles and older nonbreeders in any species is difficult because of dispersal in juveniles and wandering in older nonbreeders. In cooperative breeders some of these problems are overcome by delayed dispersal, absence of nonbreeding floaters, and a large number of sedentary helpers. Estimates of nonbreeder (helper) deaths can then be estimated from the number of helpers disappearing minus the number expected to have become breeders outside the study area (Woolfenden and Fitzpatrick 1984, Koenig and Mumme 1987). Custer and Pitelka (1977) used life-table analysis to estimate juvenile survivorship; their approach is used here and extended to estimate survivorship of older nonbreeders as well.

Assumptions

Several assumptions are necessary to carry out a life-table analysis. One is that the Hastings population has a stable age distribution (e.g., Caughley 1977). Few, if any, field studies meet this criterion. Both birth and death rate of fledglings and breeders varied considerably, especially in 1983–1984. However, if viewed over the five-year study period, the Hastings breeding population was relatively stable. It follows that the population's net reproductive rate (R_o) was approximately 1.0.

From a life table based on breeders, nonbreeder survivorship can be estimated, given that $R_o = 1$. This can be corrected further by checking the values against observed values, including the age that jays acquired a territory for the first time, and the proportion of territorial jays that were yearlings. With these checks the life table represents a reasonable model for the Hastings population. The life tables further allow estimation of other demographic variables considered to be important factors leading to cooperative or noncooperative social systems.

Life-table parameters

The proportion of each age class that acquires a territory can be estimated from the age distribution of jays acquiring a territory for the first time, the number of territory vacancies available for each age class of nonbreeder, and the number of jays competing for the vacancies.

The age distribution of males and females acquiring a territory for the first time (Fig. 14) are conservative estimates in which older age classes are probably under represented. Females filled vacancies earlier than males, with 50% of 34 territory vacancies taken by first-year females and 29% of 27 vacancies taken by first-year males. The oldest known female was three and the oldest known male four, but again, because the study lasted only five years the oldest known novice could only be four years old.

The number of breeding opportunities each year is determined by the mortality rate of breeders, and thus, in part, by turnover in territory occupants. Counting the mean annual number of openings in the population would underestimate the number of available vacancies because six more territories were lost than were added over the study period. I assumed that over time breeder density would have stabilized at prior levels. To calculate

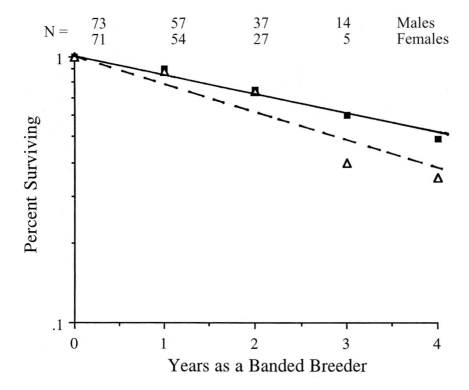

FIGURE 37. Survivorship of breeding California Scrub-Jays plotted as the proportion of banded breeders surviving from 1 to 4 years after banding. Sample sizes above points are the number of individuals at risk during the period and include breeders of all ages. The lines represent constant survivorship of 0.83% per year for males and 0.79% per year for females.

the number of vacancies I used the mean mortality rate, which averaged 16.6% for males and 22.1% for females (Table 20). Because female breeders have a higher mortality rate, more vacancies are available to and filled by first-year females.

The next step is to determine the number of individuals competing for these vacancies. The earliest age at which a jay could acquire a territory was set at 10 months, although a few jays may do so by six months. Survivorship from fledging to one month averaged 72% (Table 11). Past this age for unsettled young and older floaters survivorship was estimated iteratively using various combinations of survivorship values. Numerous combinations are possible, but lowering one value (e.g., juvenile survivorship) necessitates raising the other (e.g., older floater survivorship) to satisfy the conditions specified above. Survivorship values from one month to one year of 60% for both sexes, and 72% and 75% for older nonbreeding females and males, respectively, provided the most reasonable estimates.

The estimated number of male and female nonbreeders in each age class (Table 22) is dependent on age-specific survivorship and territory vacancies. For example, a hypothetical population of 1,000 pairs produces 1,200 fledglings (1.2 per pair; Table 10), half of which are males and half females. These fledglings survive to one year at 0.43 (0.72 survivorship to one month postfledging ×0.6 survivorship from one month to one year), when they either acquire a territory or become floaters. Each year there are 166 vacancies for males and 210 for females (1,000 × annual mortality rate). These vacancies are filled by different age classes in the proportions found on the study area (Fig. 14b). For example, 50% (105) of the 210 vacancies for females are filled by first-year jays, 37.5% (79) by two-year olds, and 12.5% (26) by three-year olds. Juvenile and older nonbreeder survivorship was adjusted so that all surviving females hold territories in their third year.

These data further allow calculations of the proportion of each age class that is territorial (P_{tx}), and the age-specific probability of acquiring a territory (P_{bx}; Table 22). Under the conditions outlined above, 40% of first-year, 83% of second-year, and 100% of third-year females are territorial, compared to 19% of first-year, 52% of second-year, 75% of third-year, and 100% of fourth-year males. These values reflect those actually observed: 12 jays banded as nestlings prior to 1984 acquired breeding status on the study area, 5 (42%) in their first year, 4 (33%) their second year, and 3 (25%) in their third year (Table 2).

However, only 8.7% of territorial first-year females and 40% of territorial first-year males bred, and after the acorn crop failure 32% of adult pairs failed to lay (Table 11). P_{tbx} (the proportion of each age class breeding) reflects this by reducing P_{tx} (the proportion territorial) by the relevant amounts for each age class.

In the Hastings population, fecundity of territorial jays (f_x) increased with age (Table 18, Fig. 35), but these data slightly exaggerate average fledgling production because most of the data for older jays were obtained in 1985, a year of good reproduction; f_x values were, therefore, reduced by approximately 5% for the four- and five-year old age classes. The values in column f_x of the life table further differ from the values in Table 18, because f_x values in the life table are for jays that initiated breeding. Because not all jays bred, m_x (the average fecundity of all jays of age-class x) equals f_x (the average fecundity of breeders of age class x) multiplied by P_{tbx} (the proportion of each age class breeding). The maximum age of jays was set at 15.

TABLE 22. CALCULATING AGE THAT SCRUB-JAYS FIRST ACQUIRE TERRITORIES

Age (x)	Survivorship		Age of territory aquisition (A_x)	Number of			Proportion territorial (Pt_x)	Probability of getting territory (Pb_x)
	Breeders (Sb_x)	Floaters (Sf_x)		Vacancies (Ob_x)	Nonbreeders (Nf_x)	Breeders (Nb_x)		
Females								
Fledge	—	0.72	0	0[a]	600[b]	0	0	0
1 month	—	0.60	0	0	434	0	0	0
1 year	0.79	0.72	0.50	105	156	105	0.40	0.40
2 years	0.79	0.72	0.38	7	33	162	0.83	0.70
3 years	0.79	0.72	0.12	26	−2[c]	152	1.00	1.00
Males								
Fledge	—	0.72	0	0	600	0	0	0
1 month	—	0.60	0	0	434	0	0	0
1 year	0.83	0.75	0.29	49	212	49	0.19	0.19
2 years	0.83	0.75	0.37	61	96	102	0.52	0.39
3 years	0.83	0.75	0.17	28	44	129	0.75	0.39
4 years	0.83	0.75	0.17	28	+5[c]	136	1.00	1.00

Note: Values for breeder survivorship from Table 20; nonbreeders survivorship from life-table calculations; age distribution of scrub-jays filling territory vacancies from Figure 14b.

[a] Number of vacancies based upon a hypothetical population of 1,000 pairs, with all vacancies created by breeder deaths.

[b] Number of fledglings based upon 1,000 pairs producing 1.2/pair (Table 10).

[c] There were no excess female floaters (-2) in year 3, and 5 excess males floaters in year 4.

The Life Tables

Several assumptions used in deriving the life-table values warrant closer examination. First, many of the variables are estimates based on five-year averages. Mean breeder survivorship and reproductive output may actually be higher than observed because of the poor success in 1983–1984. Second, true survivorship rates of floating juvenile and adult nonbreeders is unknown. Such data are crucial for resolving questions concerning the costs and benefits of floating. Third, the demographic estimates are based upon 50 pairs of jays living in relatively high-quality habitat that attracted, in good acorn years, floaters from a wide area and fledged large numbers of independent young. For the life table, the study area was treated as a "closed system" such that the number of nonbreeders competing for the vacancies were those produced by the local breeders and the number of vacancies that opened were those resulting from the breeders' deaths. The implications of a regional (and more realistic) view are discussed below.

Although based on several assumptions, the life-table models for females (Table 23) and males (Table 24) closely fit observed population parameters. For example, all females breed by their third year (identical to observed), 10.7% of all territorial females are first-year birds (10.7% observed), and the total number of territorial jays in the life table ($\sum (l_x)(P_{tx})$) produces 1,000 fledglings, which equals 1.2 fledglings per pair (the overall average for the population; Table 10). Values for males are similarly close to those observed in the population.

The known age structure of the population in 1985 is shown in Table 25. In 1985, the exact ages of 37 (41%) of the 90 breeders were known. Because of the short duration of the study, known age older jays are few. Nevertheless, 22% of female breeders were known to be five years or older, and 45% of male breeders. The oldest known male was at least nine and the oldest female at least five.

Estimated age-specific reproductive value (V_x) and the contribution each age class makes to the net reproductive rate ($\sum l_x m_x$) are presented in Figure 38. The values are similar for males and females, despite the earlier age at which females acquire territories, because of the low reproductive success of young breeders, particularly first-year females, and the higher survivorship of male breeders. Reproductive value and $l_x m_x$ of males and females reaches a peak at age four, due to both delayed breeding and low fecundity and reproductive success of young territorial jays.

Estimating Life-time Reproductive Success

Mean life-time reproductive success (LRS) may be estimated from the life table as estimated LRS= $\sum l_x m_x$, where l_x and m_x are age-specific survivorship and fecundity (same sex fledglings per breeder) from breeding age (≥ 1) through age 15, the assumed reproductive life. Thus, LRS equals the expected number of same sex fledglings produced by an individual.

LRS estimates for males and females that acquire territories as yearlings, at age two, and as modeled in the life tables are given in Table 26. A female acquiring a territory at age one can expect to fledge 2.60 female offspring over her lifetime, and a male 3.17 male offspring. (These values can be doubled for total fledglings produced). Male LRS is higher due to slightly higher survivorship. How does a delay in breeding affect these LRS estimates? A female that delays breeding (floats) for a year and then acquires a territory at age two can expect to fledge 2.31 females, 11% fewer than a female acquiring a territory at age one. Because fecundity of territorial first-year females is only 0.04 fledglings,

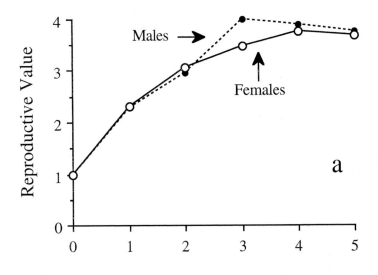

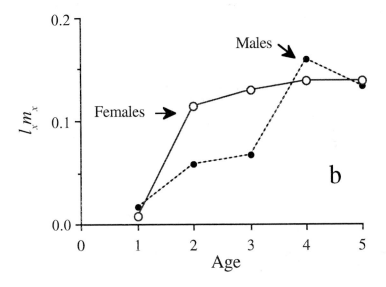

FIGURE 38. Life table estimates of reproductive value and $l_x m_x$. (a) Reproductive value (in fledglings) of males and females, and (b) $l_x m_x$ (the contribution each age class makes to the total reproductive output of the population).

the decline is due almost entirely to the probability of dying before breeding (survivorship is estimated to be higher for breeders than floaters). A male that delays breeding until age two produces 2.72 male fledglings, a 14% decline.

However, dispersing scrub-jays may be forced to delay breeding and float for several years; as modeled in the life tables, estimated LRS, discounted for age-specific probability (from age one onward) of acquiring a territory (Table 22) and the probability of dying, equals 2.42 fledglings for females (9.6% less than females acquiring territories as

TABLE 23. FEMALE LIFE TABLE ($R_o = 1.004$)

Age x	S_{xb}	S_{xf}	S_x	l_x	P_{tbx}	f_x	m_x	$l_x m_x$	Age structure Total	Breeders
Fledge		0.724	0.724	1.000	0.000	0.000	0.000	0.000		
1 month		0.600	0.600	0.724	0.000	0.000	0.000	0.000		
1 year	0.79	0.720	0.748	0.434	0.035	0.500	0.018	0.008	0.228	0.110
2-yr	0.79	0.720	0.778	0.325	0.769	0.458	0.352	0.115	0.170	0.169
3-yr	0.79	0.720	0.790	0.253	0.927	0.555	0.515	0.130	0.133	0.159
4-yr	0.79	0.720	0.790	0.200	0.927	0.750	0.695	0.139	0.105	0.125
5-yr	0.79	0.720	0.790	0.158	0.927	0.950	0.881	0.139	0.083	0.099
6-yr	0.79	0.720	0.790	0.125	0.927	0.950	0.881	0.110	0.065	0.078
7-yr	0.79		0.790	0.098	0.927	0.950	0.881	0.087	0.052	0.062
8-yr	0.79		0.790	0.078	0.927	0.950	0.881	0.069	0.041	0.049
9-yr	0.79		0.790	0.061	0.927	0.950	0.881	0.054	0.032	0.039
10-yr	0.79		0.790	0.049	0.927	0.950	0.881	0.043	0.025	0.030
11-yr	0.79		0.790	0.038	0.927	0.950	0.881	0.034	0.020	0.024
12-yr	0.79		0.790	0.030	0.927	0.950	0.881	0.027	0.016	0.019
13-yr	0.79		0.790	0.024	0.927	0.950	0.881	0.021	0.013	0.015
14-yr	0.79		0.790	0.019	0.927	0.950	0.881	0.017	0.010	0.013
15-yr	0.79		0.790	0.015	0.927	0.950	0.881	0.013	0.008	0.013

yearlings) and 2.42 for males (24% less than those acquiring territories at age one; Table 26). Males that do not acquire territories their first year incur greater costs relative to females, because a male has a lower probability of acquiring a territory at any age than a female (Table 22).

An interesting question is how estimated LRS would be affected if California Scrub-Jays delayed dispersal, remained at home, and helped. The increase in fledgling production due to a single helper in the Florida Scrub-Jay averages 51% (Woolfenden and Fitzpatrick 1984); a similar increase in the California Scrub-Jay would raise production from 1.2 to 1.8 fledglings/pair. When this increase is converted to genome-equivalents (see Brown and Brown 1981b for details of this method; these values may be doubled for

TABLE 24. MALE LIFE TABLE ($R_o = 0.998$)

Age x	S_{xb}	S_{xf}	S_x	l_x	P_{tbx}	f_x	m_x	$l_x m_x$	Age structure Total	Breeders
Fledge		0.724	0.724	1.000	0.000	0.000	0.000	0.000		
1 month		0.600	0.600	0.724	0.000	0.000	0.000	0.000		
1 year	0.834	0.750	0.766	0.434	0.075	0.500	0.038	0.016	0.200	0.051
2-yr	0.834	0.750	0.793	0.333	0.438	0.400	0.175	0.058	0.153	0.107
3-yr	0.834	0.750	0.812	0.264	0.635	0.400	0.254	0.067	0.121	0.123
4-yr	0.834	0.750	0.834	0.214	0.855	0.875	0.748	0.160	0.099	0.135
5-yr	0.834	0.750	0.834	0.179	0.855	0.875	0.748	0.134	0.082	0.112
6-yr	0.834	0.750	0.834	0.149	0.855	0.875	0.748	0.112	0.069	0.094
7-yr	0.834		0.834	0.124	0.855	0.875	0.748	0.093	0.057	0.078
8-yr	0.834		0.834	0.104	0.855	0.875	0.748	0.078	0.048	0.065
9-yr	0.834		0.834	0.086	0.855	0.875	0.748	0.065	0.040	0.054
10-yr	0.834		0.834	0.072	0.855	0.875	0.748	0.054	0.033	0.045
11-yr	0.834		0.834	0.060	0.855	0.875	0.748	0.045	0.028	0.038
12-yr	0.834		0.834	0.050	0.855	0.875	0.748	0.038	0.023	0.031
13-yr	0.834		0.834	0.042	0.855	0.875	0.748	0.031	0.019	0.026
14-yr	0.834		0.834	0.035	0.855	0.875	0.748	0.026	0.016	0.022
15-yr	0.834		0.834	0.029	0.855	0.875	0.748	0.022	0.013	0.018

TABLE 25. AGE DISTRIBUTION OF BREEDERS IN 1985

	Females (N = 45)		Males (N = 45)	
Age	Number	Percent	Number	Percent
1	8	18%	3	7%
2	3	7%		
2+	3	7%	2	4%
3	5	11%	7	16%
3+	8	18%	4	9%
4	5	11%	5	11%
4+	3	7%	4	9%
5				
5+	10	22%	12	27%
6+			1	2%
7+			4	9%
8+			2	4%
9+			1	2%

TABLE 26. ESTIMATED LIFE TIME REPRODUCTIVE SUCCESS (IN SAME SEX FLEDGLINGS) OF MALE AND FEMALE CALIFORNIA SCRUB-JAYS THAT ACQUIRE TERRITORIES AS YEARLINGS, AT AGE TWO, AND IN THE DISTRIBUTION AS MODELED IN THE LIFE TABLES

	LRS for jays acquiring territories at age			Indirect
	1-year	2-years	Life table	benefits[a]
Males	3.18	2.72	2.42	0.25
Females	2.60	2.31	2.35	0.24

[a] Hypothetical indirect benefit of helping for one year (see text for explanation).

"offspring equivalents"), the estimated indirect benefits for helping for one year equals 0.24 genome-equivalents for a single female helper and 0.25 for a single male helper. These hypothetical indirect benefits are significantly greater than the direct benefits derived from acquiring a territory and breeding status for a first-year jay. For example, a first-year female acquiring a territory will, on average, fledge 0.08 offspring (Table 18) or 0.04 genome-equivalents (and a male 0.17). This suggests that a jay would do best by helping for a year and then breeding independently rather than breeding at age one or floating, all else being equal. However, differences in survivorship on and off the natal territory and in the probability of securing a suitable territory may easily outweigh these hypothetical indirect fitness benefits (Woolfenden and Fitzpatrick 1984, Walters et al. 1992a). Analyses of life-time reproductive success for several cooperative breeders (Florida Scrub-Jays, Woolfenden and Fitzpatrick 1984; Acorn Woodpeckers, Koenig and Mumme 1987) indicate that the highest LRS is achieved by breeding as early as possible on a suitable territory. In Florida Scrub-Jays, success in acquiring a territory at an early age is, together with breeder life-span, the most important contributor to a jay's lifetime reproductive success (Fitzpatrick and Woolfenden 1988, Fitzpatrick et al. 1989).

Not surprisingly, relative survivorship of floaters and breeders and the age of first breeding are critical factors affecting estimated LRS. In their long-term study of Florida Scrub-Jays, Woolfenden and Fitzpatrick (1984; Fitzpatrick and Woolfenden 1986, 1988) concluded that the indirect benefit to nonbreeders of raising the reproductive output of relatives is small (and decreases rapidly with group size) compared to those of (1) higher survivorship on the natal territory, (2) increasing the chance of getting or creating a high-quality territory vacancy, and (3) increasing the survivorship of related breeders (see also Brown 1974, Koenig and Mumme 1987; Stacey and Ligon 1987, 1991). Hence, except for the latter benefit, the general conclusions regarding factors affecting LRS and selecting for alternative dispersal strategies in cooperative and noncooperative scrub-jays are similar. The specific ecological factors that promote delayed dispersal in one population and early dispersal and floating in another are examined below.

TEST OF THEORIES AND COMPARISONS

In this section, I compare data from the California Scrub-Jay with those from several closely related cooperative *Aphelocoma* and other cooperative breeders to test hypotheses and predictions of models for the evolution of cooperative breeding. These comparisons are used to answer the following questions: Do the models adequately explain why one species is cooperative and a closely related species or conspecific is not? What are the critical ecological, demographic, and behavioral differences that select for the alternative social systems in these species? There are, however, three potential complications in drawing conclusions based on such comparisons: (1) the models examined are for the evolution of cooperative breeding, not its loss; (2) it is difficult to separate the effects of historical vs. current ecological factors; and (3) observed behaviors may be relics of ancestral, cooperative populations.

The models discussed are for the evolution of delayed dispersal and cooperative breeding. But are the conditions hypothesized to select for the evolution of a character state such as cooperative breeding the mirror image of those leading to its loss? Not always. In *Aphelocoma* jays, phylogenetic studies reveal that cooperative breeding occurred before the diversification of the genus (Peterson and Burt 1992) and that it was lost in the western North American lineage (Pitelka 1986). Studies of *Aphelocoma* examine factors important to the maintenance of cooperative (or noncooperative) breeding rather than its evolutionary origins; current conditions may not reflect those that led to the evolution of the observed traits and would therefore not be responsible for observed differences in social behavior. For example, cooperative breeding in Australian babblers (*Pomatostomus* spp.) apparently arose in rain forest habitats (Schodde 1982) but has been maintained as the group diversified and spread into arid interior Australia; cooperative breeding still occurs but under far different ecological conditions under which it evolved. In a similar vein, noncooperative populations derived from cooperatively breeding ancestors may exhibit behaviors or demographic components that are relic of ancestral, cooperative populations. In Western Scrub-Jays these may include tolerance of young and nonbreeders on territories, delayed breeding, very low reproductive success in territorial first-year birds, and aspects of territorial acquisition.

Despite these potential complications, for the first time detailed ecological, demographic, and behavioral comparisons can be made among closely related cooperative and noncooperative species and may provide evidence of the key factors selecting for a switch from delayed dispersal and cooperative breeding to early dispersal and floating.

BROWN'S THEORY OF HABITAT SATURATION AND GROUP LIVING

Brown (1969) developed a model for the role of territorial exclusion in creating a nonbreeding surplus, and later for group living and cooperative breeding in New World jays and the genus *Aphelocoma* in particular (Brown 1974, 1978; see also Verbeek 1973). This habitat saturation (HS) theory incorporates both ecological and demographic arguments, and with various modifications and elaborations has served as the underlying framework for most other theories for the evolution of cooperative breeding in permanently territorial species.

Brown argues that in nonmigratory, long-lived species residing near carrying capacity in habitats characterized by stable mature vegetation, territory vacancies will be rare, as all suitable habitats will be "saturated." Under these conditions, the best strategy for young birds is to delay breeding and remain on their natal territory. Early dispersal and floating are not precluded, but young that delay dispersal stand a better chance of eventually getting a territory and reproducing successfully due to competitive advantages that come with increased age and experience and through territorial inheritance. And once young delay dispersal, those that "help" relatives are at selective advantage (through direct and indirect fitness benefits) over ones that do not. Advantages also accrue to breeders via decreased defense costs and enhanced reproductive success due to helper aid. In addition, larger groups have a competitive advantage over smaller ones in securing and keeping territorial space. Brown (1974) suggests that this process is self-reinforcing, leading to a build up of nonbreeders and eventually to multi-pair territories and is mirrored in the progression from the noncooperative California Scrub-Jay, to a single breeding pair with helpers as in the Florida Scrub-Jay, and finally to the multi-pair territories with helpers as in the Mexican Jay.

Brown (1974:78) listed six attributes of cooperative as compared to noncooperative breeders under the "K-selection phase" of his model: (1) delayed maturity, (2) higher survivorship, (3) lower reproductive rate, (4) reduced dispersal, (5) a higher proportion of nonbreeders, and (6) narrower habitat tolerance. These predictions are tested below with data from the California Scrub-Jay and provide a framework for exploring other hypotheses as well.

Delayed maturity and the "Skill Hypothesis"

Delayed maturation is common among cooperative breeders, but controversy exists over whether this leads to group living and cooperation per se (Skutch 1961, Lack 1966) or is merely a correlate of some other causal factor(s) (Brown 1978, Lawton and Lawton 1986). Retention of juvenile or subadult morphological characteristics for a year or two could be a consequence of delayed breeding, but such characteristics occur in both cooperative and noncooperative species (Pitelka 1945). Delayed maturation or "lack of skill" in foraging efficiency, territorial defense, predator avoidance, and reproductive skills may favor delayed breeding (Stearns and Crandell 1981; Brown 1985, 1987), and some suggest this may lead to group living and cooperative breeding as well (Skutch 1961, Rowley 1965, Lack 1966; Heinsohn et al. 1988, 1990; Heinsohn 1991).

Numerous studies have demonstrated that young of cooperative breeders are less skillful than older individuals, including those on cooperative *Aphelocoma* jays (Stallcup and Woolfenden 1978, Brown 1985, DeGange 1976, McGowan 1987), but this is also true for numerous noncooperative species that delay breeding (Sæther 1990). It is also true that young nonbreeders may learn from experienced group members (e.g., White-winged Choughs, *Corcorax melanorhamphos* [Heinsohn et al. 1988]; Seychelles Warblers, *Acrocephalus sechellensis* [Komdeur 1996]; White-throated Magpie-Jays [Langen 1996a,c; Langen and Vehrencamp 1999]; and Long-tailed Tits, *Aegithalos caudatus* [Hatchwell et al. 1999]).

Delayed maturation and overall lack of skill in young birds in both cooperative and

noncooperative breeding systems is indicated by a steep increase in age-specific reproductive success of breeders. In California Scrub-Jays, Florida Scrub-Jays, and Mexican
Jays, reproductive success is quite low at age one and increases to peak at age four or
five (Fig. 39). More California than Florida scrub-jays acquire territories as yearlings, but
few breed and those that do have very low success. Some of the few Florida Scrub-Jays
that acquired a territory their first year bred successfully (Woolfenden and Fitzpatrick
1984). In some cooperative breeders, such as the Gray-crowned Babbler (*Pomatostomus
temporalis*), the gonads are usually small and presumably nonfunctional their first year,
and do not reach full size until the third year (Brown and Brown 1981b). However, this
may be more an inability of young individuals to acquire a territory and breeding status
as young Gray-crowned Babblers that are able to acquire a territory and breed are nearly
as productive as adults (Brown and Brown 1981b).

In both the Florida Scrub-Jay (Woolfenden and Fitzpatrick 1984) and Mexican Jay
(Brown 1974), larger groups are more successful than smaller ones in securing and
expanding territorial space. Although this makes it difficult to establish and defend a
territory independently, group living and cooperative behavior may in some cases allow
young individuals to be more successful breeders than otherwise would be possible by
providing aid in feeding young, territorial defense, detecting and fighting off predators,
and nest building. For example, inexperienced Florida Scrub-Jays breeding as pairs average 1.24 fledglings/pair, mixed pairs 1.34, and experienced pairs 1.8. With helpers, the
same pairs raise 2.2, 2.5, and 2.4 fledglings, respectively; inexperienced (young) and
experienced (older) pairs with helpers fledge the same number of young (Woolfenden
and Fitzpatrick 1984).

These comparisons suggest that young in both cooperative and noncooperative birds
may be less efficient at foraging, exhibit delayed maturity, and lack reproductive skills
compared to older age classes. Although lack of skill and delayed maturity in Western
Scrub-Jays may also be relic of ancestral cooperative populations, no reason exists to
expect that differences in delayed maturity or skill have led to group living rather than
having arisen as a consequence of it.

Higher survivorship

Higher survivorship of breeders was predicted for cooperative breeders (as this contributes to lower breeder turnover and fewer breeding vacancies; see Arnold and Owens
1998, 1999) but no significant difference exists among the California and Florida scrub-
jays and Mexican Jays (Table 27), or *A. californica obscura*, another noncooperative
population (83%; M. J. Alpers, pers. comm.). Survivorship was even higher (94%) in the
Island Scrub-Jay (Atwood et al. 1990).

Lower Reproductive Rate

Reproductive rate is not related to social behavior in *Aphelocoma* jays (Table 27).
Clutch size is slightly smaller in the Florida Scrub-Jay than in either the Mexican Jay
or California Scrub-Jay, although populations of the Western Scrub-Jay in drier habitats
have significantly smaller clutch sizes overall (Atwood 1978). Fledging success is lower
in California compared to simple pairs in Florida (43% vs. 66%), and considerably lower
compared to pairs with helpers (80%).

Percentages of egg and nestling survivorship are similar. In California, 60.6% of eggs
laid hatched and 48% of hatchlings fledged. In Florida, for pairs without helpers, 60% of

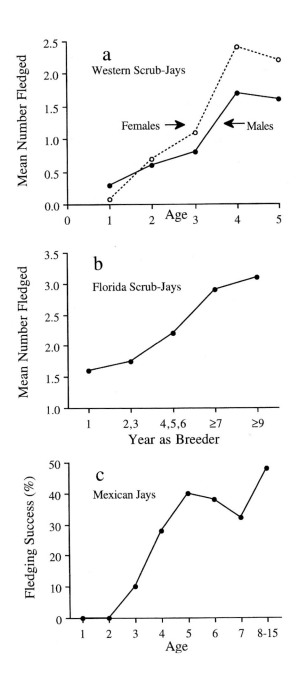

FIGURE 39. Increase in reproductive success with age for the noncooperative California Scrub-Jay, the cooperative Florida Scrub-Jay, and the Mexican Jay. (a) Age-specific reproductive success (fledgling production) in California Scrub-Jay breeders; (b) relationship between past breeding experience and fledgling production in Florida-Scrub Jays (because few first-year jays breed, the *x*-axis begins roughly at age 2; from fig. 8.15 in Woolfenden and Fitzpatrick 1984); and (c) fledging success with age in Mexican Jay breeders (from fig. 3 in Brown 1986).

eggs laid hatched and 54% of hatched eggs fledged. For pairs with helpers in Florida, corresponding values increase significantly to 69% and 68% (Woolfenden and Fitzpatrick 1984). Overall, fledgling production averaged 1.2 per pair at Hastings and 1.59 in Florida, rising to 2.31 for pairs with helpers (Woolfenden and Fitzpatrick 1984).

Given these similarities, what accounts for the higher reproductive output in Florida? First, although nest predation rates are similar, a major difference between the Florida and California populations is the rate of starvation (4.8% vs. 17.2%). Second, virtually all breeding pairs in Florida initiate breeding every year (G. Woolfenden, pers. comm.), and 13% of pairs attempt to raise second broods. At Hastings, however, in 215 breeding pair-years, 40 pairs failed to lay eggs. If these pairs are excluded, the overall average climbs to 1.5 fledglings per pair, quite close to 1.59 per pair without helpers in Florida. Third, pairs with helpers in Florida show a significant increase in fledgling production, which is attributable to lower predation rates on eggs and nestlings compared to those of unassisted pairs.

Reduced dispersal

Comparisons among *Aphelocoma* jays generally support Brown's prediction of reduced dispersal (see also Zack 1990). Mean natal to breeding territory distance in Florida Scrub-Jays is 0.9 territories for males and 3.4 for females (these distances include nearly all dispersal events). In comparison, values from scrub-jays at Hastings were 1.3 and 3.2 territories traversed for males and females; however, these data include but a small percentage of the estimated successful dispersal events. Many California Scrub-Jays float in the vicinity of their natal territories but others make wide-ranging movements and most acquired territories off the study area; hence, actual natal to breeding distances, though unknown, are certainly greater. Brown and Brown (1990) found that Mexican Jays may never leave high-quality territories or at most move to adjacent territories to breed, but their sample was small (6 territories) and evidence of immigration existed.

TABLE 27. Demographic comparisons among *Aphelocoma* jays

	Scrub-Jays			Mexican Jay[d]
	California[a]	Island[b]	Florida[c]	
Breeder survivorship	♂ 0.83	Both 0.94	Both 0.82	0.86
	♀ 0.79			0.81
Mean clutch size	3.7	3.7	3.4	4.0
Mean fledglings/pair	1.2	—	1.4 (pairs)	—
			2.4 (w/helpers)	
Percent non-breeders	♂ 29%	~50%[e]	31%	30%[e]
	♀ 16%		22%	
Age of transition to breeding status (yr)	1–3	2-3	2–3	3–4
Mean age first territorial (yr)	♂ 2.2	—	2.9	—
	♀ 1.6	—	2.4	—
Mean age first breeding (yr)	♂ 2.4	—	3.0	—
	♀ 2.1	—	2.4	—

[a] Estimates derived from demographic values as used in the life tables for females (Table 23) and males (Table 24).
[b] Data from Atwood et al. (1990); clutch size from Atwood (1980b); percent nonbreeders from an independent life table estimate.
[c] Data from Woolfenden and Fitzpatrick (1984).
[d] Data from Brown (1974, 1985, 1986) and Brown and Brown (1990).
[e] Combined estimate, not broken down by sex.

Prebreeders

A salient feature of Brown's (1974, 1978) theory is that permanently territorial non-cooperative species either should not have a significant nonbreeding surplus, or that the surplus is due to factors other than habitat saturation, such as an unbalanced sex ratio (Rowley 1965), inability of simple pairs to raise young (Rabenold 1984, 1985), or general lack of skill in young individuals (Brown 1985, 1987).

The "nonbreeding surplus" can be a significant in both cooperative and noncooperative breeders. In field experiments where breeders were removed or high-quality habitat created, breeding positions were filled by nonbreeding helpers in cooperative species (Hannon et al. 1985, Pruett-Jones and Lewis 1990, Komdeur 1991, Walters et al. 1992b) and by floaters in noncooperative species (Watson and Moss 1970, Rutberg and Rohwer 1980). A substantial percentage of nonbreeders may occur in other permanently territorial, noncooperative species, with estimates of 35% in Carrion Crows (*Corvus corone*) in Scotland (Charles 1972, as cited by Patterson 1980) to 50% in the Rufous-collared Sparrow (Smith 1978). Cooperative species also show a wide range in the percentage of nonbreeders, from a low of 8% in one population of Bicolored Wren (*Campylorhynchus griseus*; Austad and Rabenold 1985), to 25% in Acorn Woodpeckers at Hastings (Koenig and Mumme 1987), and up to 80% in the African Yellow-billed Shrike (*Corvinella corvina*; Grimes 1980).

The percentage of nonbreeders (one year and older) averaged 31% for the Florida Scrub-Jay and 30% for the Mexican Jay, compared with an estimated 22% for scrub-jays at Hastings (Table 27) and perhaps 50% on Santa Cruz Island (data calculated from Atwood 1980b, Atwood et al. 1990).

Evidence that scrub-jays at Hastings may not acquire territories for several years includes: (1) the small proportion of territorial first-year females and males (10.7% and 4.9%, respectively, N = 223 breeding years; Table 12); (2) the percentage of jays banded as nestlings that eventually acquired territories on the study area (42% did so at age one, 33% at age two, and 25% at age three (Table 2); and (3) in four of five years, floaters were present in large numbers in March through early May and had no chance of breeding. Thus, noncooperative scrub-jays can have as high, or sometimes higher, proportions of nonbreeders than their cooperative relatives.

But is the "surplus" in noncooperative populations due to other factors besides habitat saturation? In Western Scrub-Jays, the sex ratio of floaters is roughly equal, simple pairs are the breeding unit, and lack of skill does not prevent young from acquiring territories and attempting to breed given the opportunity. More to the point, neither lack of mates or skill has any bearing on whether prebreeders delay dispersal or float. A lack of mates may prevent individuals from breeding but has no bearing on whether delayed dispersal or floating would be favored. Similarly, genetic or age effects ("skill") may deter individuals from attempting to set up territories and breed independently, but are unlikely to be important in determining whether delayed dispersal or floating is favored. However, in species where a critical group size is required for successful reproduction (e.g., *Campylorhynchus* wrens), breeding as part of a simple pair is not a viable option and delayed dispersal may be favored over floating.

Habitat differences

Brown (1974) originally predicted that permanently territorial cooperative breeders should inhabit mature stable vegetation types, but later acknowledged many exceptions

(Brown 1978). Of all the *Aphelocoma*, Western Scrub-Jays occupy the greatest geographic range and diversity of habitats (Pitelka 1951, Peterson and Vargas 1992). Florida Scrub-Jays occur in periodically burned oak scrub (Woolfenden and Fitzpatrick 1984) but may also inhabit fire suppressed and suburban landscapes that include oak scrub, although the latter may function in most years as population sinks (Breininger et al. 1995, 1996). Mexican Jays mostly inhabit mature oak-pine woodland, and Unicolored Jays are found in humid tall, luxuriant hardwood forest (Pitelka 1951, Webber and Brown 1994). Even on a local level, Western Scrub-Jays use a wider variety of habitats than their relatives. For example, where Mexican Jays and scrub-jays are sympatric, the latter use habitats that are rarely used by Mexican Jays. However, in similar habitats without Mexican Jays, scrub-jays expand into the former's preferred habitat (Marshall 1957; P. Stacey, pers. comm.). Burt and Peterson (1993) found that a cooperatively breeding population of scrub-jay in Oaxaca, Mexico, used a diverse assemblage of habitats and that conversion of its natural habitat has allowed expansion of the population.

Brown's (1974) generalization that cooperative breeders inhabit "mature, stable vegetation" followed from the idea that good quality habitat had to be saturated, so that the chance of a nonbreeder finding a good territory would be low. In contrast, Brown (1974: 73) suggested that "...the [western populations of] Scrub Jay inhabits a variety of habitats, including scrubby areas and chaparral, much of which is transient and created by forest fires. ...the higher reproductive rate and wider dispersal of the Scrub Jay may be viewed as adaptations for finding and exploiting newly available suitable habitat." The key idea is that some ecological factor acts to keep breeding habitat available or "unsaturated" in noncooperative breeders. As shown in the previous section, however, the large nonbreeding surplus in Western Scrub-Jays suggests that other factors are needed to explain the loss of delayed dispersal and group living.

THE MARGINAL HABITAT HYPOTHESIS

Koenig and Pitelka (1981) proposed that for group living to evolve in permanently territorial species, not only must high-quality habitat be saturated but marginal habitat must be relatively rare with a relatively sharp division between the two. Under these conditions, territories in high-quality habitat will be continuously occupied by established groups; those of intermediate quality will relatively rarely be occupied, and offspring will have a low probability of acquiring breeding status on a suitable territory. The key factor, however, is that because of a steep gradient between good and poor habitats, young individuals attempting to breed or even subsist in unoccupied habitat face a low probability of success and are "forced" to delay dispersal and remain on their natal territories.

If, however, a large proportion of intermediate and low-quality "marginal" habitat allows young individuals either to settle on territories, or float, early dispersal is favored. Predictions of the marginal habitat hypothesis (MHH) are contrasted with those of other models in Table 28, and examined below.

The MHH not only provides an ecological explanation for habitat saturation, it attempts to explain conditions that would preclude floating and favor delayed dispersal. Studies of cooperative breeders generally supported the MHH, including field experiments in which helpers actively competed for and filled artificially created breeding vacancies (Brown et al. 1982, Hannon et al. 1985, Pruett-Jones and Lewis 1990, Komdeur 1991). Prior studies of *Aphelocoma* also fit the predictions of the model. In the Island Scrub-Jay, Atwood (1980a) found breeding habitat "saturated" and floaters, including juveniles, only in "marginal" unoccupied habitat (open grassland with scattered shrubs or young trees and low *Baccharus* thickets that would be unsuitable for floaters on the mainland). In Florida, breeding space in high-quality habitat is always filled, and juveniles have a low probability of acquiring a territory. Juveniles do wander off their natal territories and are generally tolerated by unrelated adults until their post-juvenile molt in fall (Woolfenden and Fitzpatrick 1984). Group members, both breeders and helpers, then evict virtually all non-natal juveniles and older trespassers, and juveniles return to their natal territories and become helpers. Woolfenden and Fitzpatrick (1984; Fitzpatrick and Woolfenden 1986) demonstrate that jays breeding in marginal habitat have both lower survivorship and lower production of breeding age offspring, and therefore conclude that nonbreeding juveniles and adults would also experience low survivorship compared to staying on their natal territories.

Although these patterns support the MHH, evidence from the California Scrub-Jay does not. Nonbreeders, tolerated except during the height of the breeding season, used occupied territories and aggregated in habitats with the most abundant food resources. During the breeding season, breeders evicted floaters from their territories and floaters were rarely observed. In one year (1985) floaters were evicted only from the nest area and remained in the highest quality habitats, and microhabitat use and foraging behavior of floaters was identical to that of breeders. Thus, in the California Scrub-Jay, marginal or unoccupied habitat does not appear to be a factor in allowing nonbreeders to disperse and float. Tolerance of floaters by breeders and floaters' use of occupied habitat was also found in an study of *A. c. obscura* in southern California (M. J. Alpers, pers. comm.). This tolerance, in particular that of allowing nonbreeders access to territories but not to nests, is similar to the pattern in Florida Scrub-Jays and may be a relic behavior. In other territorial species, such as the Rufous-collared Sparrow (Smith 1978), floaters sneak through territories, which again suggests that floating does not depend on unoccupied or marginal areas for dispersal.

The MHH may explain higher levels of delayed dispersal and larger group sizes under different ecological conditions in cooperative breeders, but fails as a general explanation as to why another population is noncooperative (i.e., why nonbreeders float) for several reasons. The MHH predicts that the shape of the distribution in territory-habitat quality is fundamental. For example, Acorn Woodpecker territories at Hastings exhibit a steep territory-habitat gradient curve (little marginal habitat) and the birds are highly social

TABLE 28. PREDICTIONS OF ECOLOGICAL MODELS FOR THE EVOLUTION OF DELAYED DISPERSAL, GROUP LIVING, AND COOPERATIVE BREEDING (HS = HABITAT SATURATION[a]; MHH = MARGINAL HABITAT HYPOTHESIS[b]; FSJ = FLORIDA SCRUB-JAY MODEL[c]; EC = ECOLOGICAL CONSTRAINTS[d]; RCW = RED-COCKADED WOODPECKER MODEL[e]; BOP = BENEFITS OF PHILOPATRY[f]; WSJ=WESTERN SCRUB-JAYS[g])

Predictions	HS	MHH	FSJ	EC	RCW	BOP	WSJ
Habitat saturated?	yes	yes	yes	yes	—	no	yes
Level of breeding constraints critical?	yes	no	yes	yes	yes	no	no
Floating ecologically constrained?	no	yes	yes	yes	no	no	no
Benefits of philopatry of primary importance?	yes	no	no	no	—	yes	no
Variance in rank order of territory quality	high	low	low	?	?	high	low

[a] Brown (1974, 1978, 1987).
[b] Koenig and Pitelka (1981), Koenig and Mumme (1987).
[c] Woolfenden and Fitzpatrick (1984), Fitzpatrick and Woolfenden (1986).
[d] Emlen (1982a).
[e] Walters et al. (1992b).
[f] Stacey and Ligon (1987, 1991).
[g] This study.

(Koenig and Mumme 1987); in New Mexico where a shallow gradient exists, group size is smaller. However, even in the latter, floating appears to be infrequent. Floating in cooperative breeders is usually rare (<5%; Woolfenden and Fitzpatrick 1984, Koenig and Mumme 1987, Brown 1987, Walters 1990). Further, Woolfenden and Fitzpatrick (1990) found nonbreeders "declining" available breeding space in high-quality habitat, and the presence of available but unused "suitable" territorial space in cooperative breeders is difficult to reconcile with a strict reading of the MHH (see also Stacey and Ligon 1991).

Under what habitat gradient (range of habitat conditions) is floating precluded? In Florida Scrub-Jays (Woolfenden and Fitzpatrick 1984), Acorn Woodpeckers in both California (Koenig and Mumme 1987) and New Mexico (Stacey and Ligon 1987), and other cooperative breeders (e.g., Grey-backed Shrikes, *Lanius excubitorius* [Zack and Ligon 1985b]), some unoccupied lower quality habitat is usually available. For example, Florida Scrub-Jays breeding in overgrown scrub fledge as many young as do unassisted pairs in high-quality habitat, although fledgling survival is lower in the former habitat due possibly to higher predation pressures (Woolfenden and Fitzpatrick 1984). If overgrown scrub can support successful breeding, floating should also be possible, although higher predation rates may also apply to floaters in this habitat (G. Woolfenden, pers. comm.). Indeed, nonbreeders in Florida do occasionally disperse into unoccupied habitats, forming small flocks that may persist for a month or two (Woolfenden and Fitzpatrick 1984).

Adults may force their offspring off territories even when marginal habitat may not be present. An extreme example is the Red Grouse (=Willow Ptarmigan, *Lagopus lagopus*), where nonbreeders are evicted from breeding habitats and are forced into areas where survivorship is so low that few survive through the winter (Watson and Moss 1970, Watson 1985).

Finally, the MHH also fails to explain how floating, and delayed dispersal and helping, could coexist as alternative strategies in the same population. In Purple Gallinules (*Gallinula martinica*), juveniles help but nonbreeding adults float in nonbreeding habitat (Hunter 1987). Young Green Jays (*Cyanocorax yncas*) in Texas delay dispersal for 15 months and assist their parents in defending the territory, but the nonbreeders are evicted after the next year's offspring are fledged (Gayou 1986) and evidently float until a vacancy is located. White-throated Magpie-Jay males disperse and a substantial number may float in unoccupied habitat, whereas most females are philopatric (Innes and Johnston 1996, Langen 1996b). In a population of western American Crows, Caffrey (1992) found that nonbreeders could delay dispersal, float, or switch between the two. The best documented example is the Australian Magpie (Carrick 1963, 1972; Veltman 1989), where some nonbreeders float in nonbreeding habitat and others remain on group territories.

THE FLORIDA SCRUB-JAY MODEL

Woolfenden and Fitzpatrick (1984, Fitzpatrick and Woolfenden 1986) developed a demographic model for the evolution of cooperative breeding in the Florida Scrub-Jay and the other *Aphelocoma*. Three variables are crucial to their model: D_o, the probability that early dispersers will become established successfully as breeders; B, the summed annual probabilities that a surviving helper remaining on its natal territory will encounter or create a breeding vacancy it can successfully fill; and L_h, the survival rate of a helper at home. The model predicts that as B and L_h increase, relative to early dispersal, delayed breeding and group living will be favored so long as D_o is low, even without any indirect fitness benefits (Table 28). In the Florida Scrub-Jay, D_o is low (high constraints on independent breeding); L_h is high (in comparison to that estimated for early dispersants floating in marginal overgrown scrub or sneaking through hostile occupied territories); and B is large, for males at least, due to territorial budding (Woolfenden and Fitzpatrick 1984).

Because the model does not include floating as an option, it assumes that nearly all Western Scrub-Jays breed as yearlings. Woolfenden and Fitzpatrick (1984:339) predict that D_o values for Western Scrub-Jays are high enough to favor early dispersal: "a wide range of acceptable habitats means that dispersing juveniles need only to stay alive in order to be more or less certain of obtaining space in which to breed as yearlings." D_o values, estimated from life-table variables, provide an index of breeding space competition (see Fitzpatrick and Woolfenden 1986). Similar D_o estimates for California, Island, and Florida scrub-jays, and for other taxa (Table 29) suggest that the level of breeding constraints per se is not sufficient to explain why one population is cooperative and another noncooperative; in fact, the level of breeding constraints provides absolutely no clue as to a population's social organization. More meaningful comparisons in D_o values could be made using fledgling production from simple pairs only; the added increment in fledgling production of breeders attributable to helpers may be important in the maintenance of delayed dispersal and cooperative breeding, but these secondarily derived benefits should not be used to assess the importance of breeding constraints leading to its evolution. When D_o is calculated for pairs only, this lowers the values for cooperative breeders, further blurring any relationship between breeding constraints and breeding system (Table 29).

L_h (adult helper-survivorship) and B (probability of a helper acquiring a breeding vacancy), on the other hand, may be much different between Florida and Western scrub-jays; unfortunately, both are impossible to measure for noncooperative species. Woolfenden and Fitzpatrick (1984, 1990) present a convincing argument why L_h may be relatively high compared to early dispersal in Florida. However, in California the converse may be true because jays can float, or even settle temporarily, in high-quality, occupied habitats as well as float and merely move through marginal ones. B (the summed annual probability of finding or creating a breeding vacancy) for Western Scrub-Jays, as for female Florida Scrub-Jays (which do not benefit from territorial budding, rarely inherit territories, and disperse farther), is even harder to evaluate; however, an increase in B in Florida Scrub-Jays must be a secondarily derived benefit of group living, rather than a primary casual factor.

The Florida Scrub-Jay model overemphasizes the importance of breeding constraints in the evolution of delayed dispersal, but provides valuable insight into the role of relative survivorship of nonbreeders pursing different strategies and other demographic factors. However, it falls short in its application to noncooperative populations simply because the model considers only two options for young birds: (1) disperse and breed, or (2) stay and delay breeding. The third option, floating, is not considered.

Walters et al. (1992a) applied a similar demographic model to empirical data from Red-cockaded Woodpeckers to evaluate fitness payoffs of young males that "depart and search" (DAS) for territories and those that "stay and foray"(SAF); all females employ the former strategy. Of males surviving to age one, 31% employed the DAS strategy and of these 39% became breeders on territories; 56% were solitary on territories and an estimated 5% remained as floaters. Walters et al. estimate that mean fitness for males

TABLE 29. INDEX OF BREEDING SPACE COMPETITION[a] FOR NONCOOPERATIVE CALIFORNIA AND ISLAND SCRUB-JAYS, COOPERATIVE FLORIDA SCRUB-JAYS, AND TWO OTHER COOPERATIVE BREEDERS

Species	Sex	Breeding space competition	
		Overall (with helpers)	Pairs only
Scrub-Jay			
California	Male	—	0.31 (0.23)[b]
	Female	—	0.54 (0.43)
Island	Both	—	0.07[c]
Florida	Both	0.27	0.44[d]
Acorn Woodpeckers	Male	0.08	0.09[e]
	Female	0.21	0.25
Green Woodhoopoes	Male	1.10	5.30[f]
	Female	0.43	0.92

[a] Lower values indicate higher levels of competition; a value of 0.1 would mean one breeding vacancy for every 9 nonbreeders.

[b] Values for breeder, juvenile, and adult nonbreeder survivorship as used in life tables (Table 23 and 24), where adult nonbreeder survivorship is 10% less than that of breeders; values in parenthesis are assuming nonbreeder survivorship equals breeder survivorship.

[c] Value calculated assuming 94% breeder survivorship (Atwood et al. 1990), adult nonbreeder survivorship 20% less than breeder survivorship, and juvenile survivorship and fecundity the same as for the Hastings population.

[d] Calculated from data in Woolfenden and Fitzpatrick (1984).

[e] Calculated from data in Koenig and Mumme (1987).

[f] Calculated from data in Ligon and Ligon (1978) and Ligon (1981).

employing the two strategies is nearly equal even without indirect fitness benefits as the potential advantage of early reproduction in DAS is balanced by a low probability of successful dispersal and increased survival in those adopting SAF. Walters et al. identify four variables that may be responsible for a reduced payoff in DAS relative to noncooperative species: (1) a high survivorship in males adopting SAF compared to birds in noncooperative species; (2) a low probability of surviving DAS birds attaining breeding status; (3) poor performance of males that do attain breeding status at a young age; and (4) a striking increase in reproductive success with age. These variables are nearly identical to those identified by Emlen (1982:32) as the key factors in favoring delayed dispersal and that "Such situations are expected to be rare, and philopatry (remaining at home) should occur only when the option of early personal reproduction is severely constrained." As noted before, these attributes were shown to differ little between cooperative and noncooperative *Aphelocoma*.

THE BENEFITS OF PHILOPATRY MODEL

Stacey and Ligon (1987) developed a model for the evolution of cooperative breeding in Acorn Woodpeckers that they term the benefits of philopatry (BOP) model. Based on their long-term study of Acorn Woodpeckers in New Mexico, they concluded that, contrary to previous models (Table 28), all suitable habitats are not saturated and no sharp gradient exists between good and poor habitats. Accordingly, nonbreeders remain on high-quality territories because helping for up to three years, and then breeding on a high-quality territory, accrues higher LRS than early dispersal and independent breeding on a territory of lower quality.

Similar results, albeit with a different interpretation, were found by Fitzpatrick and Woolfenden (1988) and Fitzpatrick et al. (1989). Analyses of life-time reproductive success in Florida Scrub-Jays indicate that the highest LRS is achieved by breeding as early as possible on a suitable territory; success in acquiring a territory at an early age is, together with breeder life-span, the most important contributor to a jay's lifetime reproductive success. However, when lifetime fitness is compared for Florida Scrub-Jays breeding in different habitats, they found that jays could delay breeding for several years in the good habitat and still have higher fitness than early breeders in the poor habitat (overgrown scrub). Thus, in both Florida Scrub-Jays and Acorn Woodpeckers, individuals that breed early in the always available but less suitable habitats will have lower life-time fitness than individuals delaying dispersal but eventually breeding on better territories, assuming the choice of a territory is final and permanent. Fitzpatrick and Woolfenden see this as a high cost of early dispersal, whereas Stacey and Ligon see it as a high benefit of philopatry (i.e., opposite sides of the same coin). Interestingly, when Fitzpatrick et al. (1989) examined how the production of breeding descendants varied within high-quality habitat, profound differences became evident; some areas showed much higher production of breeding descendants than others. Although this may result from differences in individual (genetic) quality, if it is due to long-term differences in habitat, then high-quality habitats are passed down through families, resulting in high variation in the success of different lineages (Brown 1974, Fitzpatrick et al. 1989). Such variation in habitat quality would lend support to the variance hypothesis and some of Brown's predictions (Table 28). However, Fitzpatrick et al. (1989) could find no evidence that individuals differentially compete for these areas, a necessary requisite for the BOP model.

Stacey and Ligon (1991; see also Waser 1988, Powell 1989) propose that natal philopatry is favored when a high and stable variance exists in territory quality, and/or group size affects the quality of a breeding opportunity. Under the BOP hypothesis, young in small groups on high-quality territories should delay dispersal in anticipation of inheriting breeding space, whereas young born into very large groups or on low-quality territories should disperse and breed as soon as possible. If group size is critical, nonbreeders should remain only in groups of some critical mass that assures the groups of high reproductive success and survivorship. For example, in *Campylorhynchus* wrens (Rabenold 1984, 1985; Austad and Rabenold 1985, Zack and Rabenold 1989), reproductive success of pairs is near zero and increases with group size so that reproductive output (per capita) peaks in groups of either three (*C. griseus*) or four (*C. nuchalis*). In these species, nonbreeders are effectively prevented from independent breeding by high nest predation rates, and neither habitat saturation nor differences in territory quality are implicated (Austad and Rabenold 1985). Under these conditions, floating is not precluded, but the advantages of group living and helping for nonbreeders make floating, or even breeding in simple pairs, a poor alternative.

The BOP model predicts that young in noncooperative species should disperse at independence either because: (1) the habitat is more uniform and territories are of similar quality; (2) interterritory quality fluctuates unpredictably over time (therefore high-quality territories are not "inheritable"); or (3) individuals do not benefit from living in groups.

Despite such clear examples of species that may form groups because of "group-living effects," two problems exist with this suggestion. First, the BOP hypothesis does not clearly distinguish between primary and secondary group-living effects. For example, Stacey and Ligon (1991) suggest that Florida Scrub-Jays and other cooperatively breeding New World jays delay dispersal because of anti-predator benefits of group living. The orchestrated sentinel system (McGowan and Woolfenden 1989) and other group behaviors in Florida Scrub-Jays may lessen predation; pairs with helpers do experience lower nest predation rates (Schaub et al. 1992). Another group-living effect is territorial expansion with increased group size in Florida Scrub-Jays. This not only lessens any adverse impact from resource depression, but allows for territorial "budding," which Woolfenden and Fitzpatrick (1984) identify as an important factor in maintaining co-operative breeding in the Florida population. Such secondarily derived benefits may be substantive but cannot be attributed as a primary cause of delayed dispersal, although they may be important in its maintenance (current utility). Because it is always possible to point to some benefit of group living, one cannot suggest that another population is noncooperative because group benefits do not apply.

Other predictions of the BOP concern how variance in territory quality differs among populations that vary in social behavior. To date, tests have involved comparisons be-tween widely separated populations of cooperative species (e.g., Acorn woodpeckers in California and New Mexico; Koenig and Mumme 1987, Stacey and Ligon 1987). A more appropriate test can be between the closely related Western and Florida scrub-jays. Scrub-jay territories at Hastings were ranked from Type 1 to Type 3 on the basis of oc-cupancy rate and vegetation characteristics. Of approximately 45 territories (range of 40 to 52 over the study period), five (~11%) were of very low quality. In Florida, the quality of the habitat depends on whether it has been burned recently, but all of the area in the periodically burned scrub is continuously occupied in nearly all years (therefore Type 1 and Type 2 territories). Fledgling production over the study area at Hastings also appears to be more variable than in Florida. In Figure 40, both the Hastings and Florida study areas are arbitrarily divided into 9 parts. Within high-quality habitat, fledgling produc-tion is relatively uniform in Florida, ranging from 1.9 to 2.2 (Woolfenden and Fitzpatrick 1984), whereas in California it ranged from 0.6 to 1.4.

While this suggests greater variance in territory and habitat quality in the noncoop-erative population, it could be argued that the "marginal" unburned, overgrown scrub in Florida should be included, despite the fact that unburned scrub is rarely colonized but rather "grows up" and eventually takes over what was formerly high-quality habitat. Stacey and Ligon (1991) suggest that comparisons of high- and low-quality habitat in Florida would reveal marked variation in habitat-territory quality, implying that this would run counter to both the Florida Scrub-Jay model (Woolfenden and Fitzpatrick's 1984) and the MHH (Koenig and Pitelka 1981). However, one could argue that this difference is exactly the basis for the latter model (a steep drop-off in quality in rarely occupied, marginal habitats). The fact that these low-quality habitats are not continu-ously "saturated" only refutes Koenig and Pitelka and Woolfenden and Fitzpatrick to the extent one stretches the definition of "suitability," and once again illustrates the problem in defining "suitable" and "marginal" habitats (see also Koenig et al. 1992). In a study of Florida Scrub-Jays at the Kennedy Space Center, where habitat is generally more marginal, Breininger et al. (1995) found that some areas acted as source populations and others as population sinks. All areas may appear "saturated," but only because of im-migration from source habitats. Over a three-year period, demographic performance was related to landscape features; as at Archbold, open scrub oak was higher quality habitat, but territories also included a matrix of low-quality and unsuitable habitat.

According to the BOP, a shortcoming of prior analyses is that they compared habitat, not territory, quality (Stacey and Ligon 1991). For delayed dispersal to be favored under the BOP, high-quality territories must be inheritable, i.e., long-term differences in qual-ity on a per-territory basis. Early dispersal will occur in situations with low variance in territory quality, which can arise either by very low correlation and large differences in quality among years, or high correlation but uniform quality among years. For example,

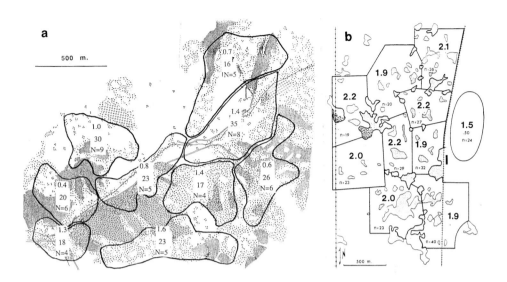

FIGURE 40. Variation in fledgling production over nine randomly drawn geographic segments of the California and Florida scrub-jay study areas. (a) California Scrub-Jay study area at the Hastings Reservation, (b) Florida Scrub-Jay study area at the Archbold Biological Station (from Woolfenden and Fitzpatrick 1984). Numbers are overall mean fledgling production calculated by averaging mean fledgling production for all breeding pairs (or family groups) on each territory in each area; N = breeding-pair years in each area.

Waser (1988), in relating philopatry to variance in home range quality, hypothesized that the banner-tailed kangaroo rat (*Dipodmys spectabilis*) dispersed, despite all other conditions favoring philopatry, because no correlation existed between home range quality among years.

However, as with defining "marginal habitat" under the MHH, it is not clear how much or little variance is required to favor one social system over another. Also, interterritory comparisons among cooperative and noncooperative species are difficult to make for several reasons. Because territories are occupied and defended by groups in cooperative species, and better territories are more continuously occupied by larger groups, this may result in more stable boundaries and greater permanence of groups on higher quality territories, and combines (and confounds) group effects with effects of territory quality. In noncooperative populations, because only pairs occupy territories, no group effects occur and territory boundaries often fluctuate upon the death of one of the breeders. The BOP model also assumes that the choice of a territory is permanent. However, movements in noncooperative breeders from low-quality to higher quality habitat may be common (e.g., Great Tits, *Parus major* [Krebs 1971]; Eurasian Magpies [Baeyens 1981]). At Hastings, 20% of all territory vacancies were filled by breeders changing territories. This suggests that young nonbreeders are able to breed initially in low or intermediate quality habitat and later acquire a better site. In cooperative breeders, on the other hand, young that disperse to low-quality habitats may not be able to shift back because nondispersing individuals are present to fill vacancies on territories in high-quality habitats. A third problem involves scale; the MHH generally examines habitat gradients over a wide geographic area, whereas BOP focuses on interterritory differences within a small, local area.

DELAYED DISPERSAL THRESHOLD MODEL

None of the models (Table 28) are fully supported by comparisons among the cooperative and noncooperative *Aphelocoma*. Most treat only two options (disperse and breed or stay and delay breeding) and sidestep the question of floating. In populations where floaters are restricted to the same degree as helpers from independent breeding, the relevant comparisons are between early dispersal (and floating) vs. delayed dispersal (and helping), not between delayed dispersal and independent breeding. The Delayed Dispersal Threshold Model (Koenig et al. 1992) addressed some of the short comings of the previous models by giving equal treatment to early dispersal and floating, delayed dispersal and helping, and independent breeding. Rather than specific predictions, the model provides a general guide for organizing and evaluating the relative importance of ecological factors under which the different dispersal strategies, including floating, are favored. The model lists 13 factors influencing the dispersal options available to offspring, most of which have been discussed in the context of the other models. Here, I focus closely on how three factors—resource depression on territories, habitat available for floating, and habitat variability—influence dispersal options in *Aphelocoma* jays and show why floating is the preferred option in Western Scrub-Jays.

Resource depression on territories

Models developed by Waser (1981, 1988) and Brown (1982, 1987) explore the relationship of territory quality and resource depression to group living. If territories have limited resources or low rates of resource renewal, the addition of individuals beyond the breeding pair may lower survival and reproductive success to such a degree that breeders should evict offspring, or offspring should choose to leave, or both. Where resource renewal is slow, group size may be limited to pairs despite other factors favoring retention of offspring. Nonbreeders may, however, increase the fitness of breeders by helping to defend the territory, or by helping to raise young. These secondarily derived benefits may lower the absolute costs to breeders of allowing offspring to remain. Lowered defense costs were used by Brown (1969) to explain why adults would tolerate young in Mexican Jays and other cooperative breeders. In contrast, on high-quality territories, specifically those with rapid resource renewal or those with "nondepreciable resources" (Waser 1988), additional group members will have relatively little effect on survival and reproductive success.

Does resource depression explain the different patterns of territorial behavior, dispersal, and group living in *Aphelocoma* jays? Both territory size and habitat productivity contribute to resource levels, but data on the latter are scant. Comparisons of territory size suggest that on large territories resource levels are lower per unit area, more patchy, or fluctuate more strongly. In this context, it is noteworthy that in Florida, scrub-jay territories are extremely large (mean of 7.2 ha for pairs and increasing significantly with group size; Woolfenden and Fitzpatrick 1984) compared to those recorded for Western Scrub-Jays (1.5 to 2.5 ha). Mexican Jay territories in Arizona are extremely large (20 to 25 ha), support large groups (ranging from 5 to 22 jays), but territory size apparently does not fluctuate with group size (Brown 1987, Brown et al. 1997). Brown (1987) suggested that Mexican Jay territories are larger than needed except at peak densities, but data are lacking, particularly with respect to winter conditions. Unicolor Jay territories may be even larger; the one territory Webber and Brown (1994) were able to map in its entirety ranged between 41 and 45 ha, and was held by a group of six.

Several lines of evidence suggest that territories in Western Scrub-Jays are not of such low quality as to preclude group living. First, breeders at Hastings tolerated their own young and unrelated floaters in the nonbreeding season and, in 1985, even in the breeding season. Second, Western Scrub-Jays occupy habitats that support group-living Mexican Jays when the latter are absent. Third, acorns, an important resource for *Aphelocoma* jays, are unlikely to limit group size because they are a "time-limited" resource (Waser 1988); processes other than consumption by scrub-jays limit their availability. Acorns remain on oaks for several months and numerous seed cachers and seed predators remove acorns before and after seed fall. In most years, acorns are superabundant with respect to a jay's (or an aggregation of jays) ability to eat or cache them, and this decreases the cost of sharing a territory either with related offspring or unrelated floaters. Little information on insect productivity is available for comparison, but nestling starvation in Florida Scrub-Jays is extremely low, and adults (with helpers) foraged only 40% of daylight hours during the breeding season. Nestling starvation averaged 17% at Hastings and breeders foraged 70% of daylight hours, suggesting potential for resource depression effects. Additional work on food resources of these jays would be required to provide a definitive answer regarding the importance of resource depression on their dispersal options (see also Burt 1996).

Habitat available for floating

In some cooperative species, special features of their habitat can strengthen ties of helpers to home groups. For example, roost-holes in Green Woodhoopoes (*Phoeniculus purpureus*; Ligon 1988) and granaries in Acorn Woodpeckers (Koenig and Mumme 1987) appear to be critical for breeders and nonbreeders alike; when limited, offspring that either attempt to set up a territory or float will do poorly. When the critical resource is important only for breeding (e.g., nest cavities), this does not constrain floating, and some other explanation for delayed dispersal must be invoked. When breeding space itself is in some way limited, as has been suggested for the cooperative *Aphelocoma* jays, it is more difficult to pin-point the resources that make space or other habitat features critical for nonbreeders. However, a complete theory for group living in any species must include an explanation of what ecological factors make adjacent habitat unsuitable for floating by nonbreeders.

Access to high-quality habitat should result in high floater survivorship, but actual floater survivorship is unknown. Data on relative age-specific survivorship of juveniles, adult nonbreeders, and territorial jays are particularly crucial for resolving questions concerning the costs and benefits of floating. In many cooperatively breeding species, nonbreeding helpers have higher survivorship than breeders (e.g., male Florida Scrub-Jays [Woolfenden and Fitzpatrick 1984], Acorn Woodpeckers [Koenig and Mumme 1987]). In contrast, nonbreeder survivorship in noncooperative species is thought to be lower than that of breeders, due to risks of dispersal (Brown 1974, Emlen 1982), being forced into marginal habitats (Watson 1985), or not having the benefits of unrestricted access to critical resources and microhabitats (Ekman and Askenmo 1984). However, Ekman and Askenmo (1986) found that nonbreeding adult male Willow Tits (*Parus montanus*) had higher survivorship than adult male breeders.

In *Aphelocoma* jays, the types of habitat available to nonbreeders are strongly influenced by the territorial behavior of breeders. In Florida Scrub-Jays, juveniles wander and are tolerated on all territories prior to their post-juvenile molt (Woolfenden and

Fitzpatrick 1984). Later, however, they are not tolerated on non-natal territories, and either return to their natal territories (the preferred option), or move to unoccupied areas, usually non-breeding habitats. Survivorship of helpers does not stabilize at adult breeder levels until age two, but this seems to be caused primarily by the risks of dispersal forays (Woolfenden and Fitzpatrick 1984, Fitzpatrick and Woolfenden 1988). Nonbreeders in Florida must trespass occupied, hostile territories in search of breeding vacancies, or float in unoccupied habitats with high predation rates (Woolfenden and Fitzpatrick 1984, 1990) and possibly also a paucity of acorns.

At Hastings, scrub-jay breeders tolerated both offspring and unrelated floaters of all ages on their territories except in May and June, and the floaters aggregated primarily where acorns were in good supply. Most remained sedentary throughout the winter and early spring, storing and recovering acorns as did the resident territorial breeders. By late April in most years, aggregations dissolved and floaters were rarely seen until early July when some of the same individuals returned and joined independent juveniles. Their disappearance coincided with increased aggression by territorial jays, but they also disappeared from areas unoccupied by breeders. In all months but May and June, floaters had unrestricted access to the best habitats, aggregated in loose flocks, and did not invest time and energy in territory defense or reproduction, and it is possible that their survivorship may be near (or even exceed) that of breeders.

In contrast, juvenile Island Scrub-Jays move to unoccupied areas by early August as breeders aggressively exclude them, including their own offspring, from their territories (Atwood 1980a; J. Atwood, pers. comm.). Yet, they do well, even though they must encroach on territories to gain access to acorns (Atwood 1980a). Few details are available on dispersal in Mexican Jays, but young retain juvenile characteristics for several years (Brown 1963), which may extend the period of tolerance and lessen the aggression of adults (Lawton and Lawton 1986). Degree of sociality varies within the range of the Mexican Jay (Brown and Brown 1990); they occur primarily in montane oak-woodland, but no obvious habitat or vegetation feature(s), separate high- and low-quality habitats, either for breeders or potential floaters (Edwards 1986).

Habitat variability

It is necessary to attempt to separate variability on a per-territory basis from phenomena that occur on a larger scale. For example, at Hastings, territory quality (occupancy rate) was correlated with vegetation characteristics, including the number of oak species and area of oak canopy. Both of these variables are indicators of reliable acorn production on a per territory basis. Hence, on the local scale, territory quality is predictable and the relative ranking of territories probably does not vary greatly from year to year. However, on a broader regional scale in California, acorn production is highly variable and strongly affects scrub-jay population density and dispersal options. This may be a key point in the secondary loss of cooperation in Western Scrub-Jays.

Acorn production in high-quality scrub-jay habitat in Florida shows little annual and spatial variation relative to that in California. In Florida, scrub oaks form continuous, shrub-like stands covering many hectares, and each scrub oak produces few seeds. Estimated production on the average territory was 128,000 acorns, and ranged from 14,000 to 331,000 (DeGange et al. 1989). Group size ranges from 2 to 10 jays in Florida, and each jay eats and caches approximately 8,700 acorns per year. It seems probable that in the poorest acorn years demand may exceed production for some large groups, but during their 25 years of study, no complete acorn crop failure occurred on the study tract (G. Woolfenden and J. Fitzpatrick, pers. comm.). Whether acorn production declines with time since last burning in Florida scrub oak species as in some other scrub-oaks (Wolgast and Stout 1977) is not known, but this would contribute to low suitability of long unburned areas in Florida for both floaters and breeders. Relatively uniform production of acorns contributes to a situation where nonbreeders would gain little by intruding on neighboring territories, intruder pressure is slight, and territory defense is economical (DeGange et al. 1989). The rarity of acorn crop failures in Florida would also prevent the local populations crashes that occur in California, thereby eliminating the benefits of the wide-ranging movements by floaters (i.e., locating areas where acorn crop crashes have created low population densities and territory vacancies) observed in Western Scrub-Jays.

Mexican Jays and Western Scrub-Jays co-occur throughout much of their range, and although Mexican Jays locally exclude scrub-jays from their preferred habitat, both can be found in oak woodlands that are generally more typical of those in California than those in Florida, that is, with highly variable acorn production (Bock and Bock 1974, Stacey and Bock 1978). However, specific details on acorn production patterns and acorn use and dependency by jays in Arizona are not known.

On the scrub-jay study area at Hastings, the three common species of oaks are distributed as isolated individuals, extensive monotypic stands, and mixed closed-canopy forest. The oaks are generally quite large and a single tree can produce well over 400,000 acorns (W. Carmen, unpubl. data). An average scrub-jay territory at Hastings includes 0.55 ha of oak canopy and two oak species, and although acorn production per territory was not measured, acorns are probably produced far in excess of jay demand in all but the poorest years. Acorn production was highly variable among years, with relatively frequent crop failures on a local habitat level and more rarely on a regional level. Acorn crop failures resulted in territory abandonment, high mortality, emigration by breeders and floaters, and poor reproductive success the following breeding season. Early dispersal and floating allows nonbreeders to respond most efficiently to spatial and temporal variation in acorn production patterns and to locate breeding vacancies. These tactics yield three patterns: (1) localized home-range movements by floaters during the fall-early spring period in most years; (2) emigration to locate acorns during local acorn crop crashes; and (3) either local or wide-ranging movements in early spring to locate breeding vacancies, particularly to areas where population density has been reduced by acorn crop failures.

SYNOPSIS

The fundamental result of this study is that floating should be considered an important strategy for acquiring breeding space, just as is delayed dispersal and helping. When floating is ignored or treated as a one-dimensional phenomenon, not only do theories for the evolution of delayed dispersal and cooperative breeding fall short, but a interesting and complex part of the social behavior of a species is overlooked. Factors that lead to delayed dispersal in cooperative species are known to be complex and may differ substantially among species and populations, and even among individuals within populations and groups. Conditions leading to early dispersal and floating may be equally complex, as are the varied responses of floaters to these conditions. Clearly, opportunities for independent breeding are constrained in both cooperative and noncooperative populations. What then makes early dispersal and floating the preferred strategy in Western Scrub-Jays? Several factors play a part including: (1) the interplay between the pattern of habitat quality and acorn production, (2) the varied behaviors floaters may employ to exploit these resources and acquire breeding space, (3) the behavioral interactions between territorial jays and floaters, and (4) the ability of floaters to settle on low-quality territories and then as breeders to move and improve the quality of their territories. Below, I provide a synopsis of the range of scrub-jay dispersal, movement and behavioral patterns.

SCRUB-JAY DISPERSAL AND FLOATING IN CENTRAL COASTAL CALIFORNIA

Figure 41 illustrates a landscape representing an idealized mosaic of habitat qualities for scrub-jays as are found in central coastal California. Higher quality habitats occur where oak diversity is high, live oaks predominate, and insects and berries are abundant. These features are most commonly found along stream channels in the area.

Figure 41a depicts clusters of territories in high- and low-quality habitat (territories in better habitat are more tightly clustered and smaller) and the dispersal movements of floaters during the nonbreeding season (August–April). Tolerance by breeders allows floaters to aggregate in high-quality habitat where acorns are abundant and floater survivorship is expected to be high. As shown, floaters fledged in low-quality habitat move into high-quality habitat, whereas those fledged in high-quality habitat may remain on or near their natal territories; both may also move considerable distances. Floaters appear to be as dependent on cached acorns as breeders and may be closely tied to their stores during the winter. When acorns are few, jays experience significantly higher mortality, reproductive failure, and territory abandonment. Poor acorn production in local areas (e.g., X and Y in Fig. 41a) results in emigration by both offspring and a substantial number of territorial breeders. They search for locations with high acorn production in which to spend the fall-early spring period.

Beginning in April, floaters and residents are less dependent on their cached acorns as invertebrate food becomes more abundant. This seasonal pattern of food abundance may contribute to the tolerance of floaters by local, settled breeders in the winter (when acorns are superabundant), and their intolerance in the breeding season (when insect prey is important and starvation rates of nestlings are high). At this time (Fig. 41b), floaters may move out of high-quality habitat where breeding vacancies are few to potentially high-quality habitat where an interval of poor acorn production has reduced breeder density (e.g., area X), or to poor quality habitat where breeding space may be available intermittently for a number of reasons, including frequent poor acorn crops and movement of breeders from there to higher quality habitat. Surviving breeders may also return to the locations they abandoned due to poor acorn production the previous fall, only some of which are able to reestablish their territories. In such areas in high-quality habitat, occupied space is unchanged but territory size has increased (Fig. 41b area X); in low-quality habitat, territories simply may be abandoned and the space go unused (area Y). Over time breeding density returns to prior levels as new territories are established.

At the onset of the breeding season, individual floaters employ different behaviors, including establishing pseudo-territories, sneaking through territories and unoccupied habitat and, as observed in one year, moving substantial distances in large cohesive flocks (as indicated by the large arrows in Fig. 41b). Floaters also may remain in aggregations

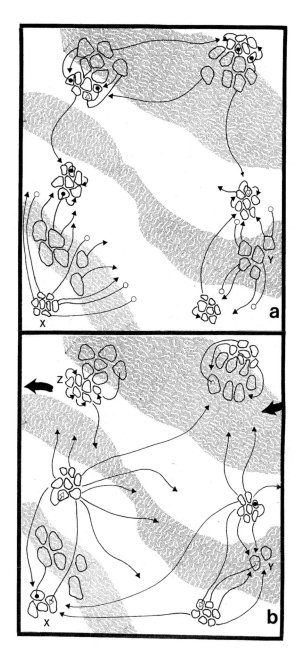

FIGURE 41. Floater and breeder (territorial jay) movements in an idealized mosaic of habitat qualities as found in central coastal California. The unshaded area represents high-quality habitat and the shaded area low-quality habitat. A few representative territories are drawn showing smaller, denser territories in high-quality habitat. Lines with closed arrows denote movement of floaters, open arrows denote floater-to-breeder transition, closed circles denote breeders changing territories, open circles denote breeders abandoning territories, and large arrows denote flock movements. Poor acorn crops occur in area X and Y with exceptional production in area Z. (a) Movement patterns during the nonbreeding season (August–April). (b) Movement patterns during the breeding season (May–July).

on high-quality habitats throughout the breeding season (e.g., area Z in Fig. 41b) as a result of increased tolerance by breeders given unusually abundant acorns into the summer months.

During the year, floaters search for and fill available breeding vacancies as shown in Figure 41. Although breeding vacancies arise from breeder death throughout suitable habitat, floaters have the greatest probability of gaining a breeding vacancy either in poor quality habitat where breeder turnover may be greater or in high-quality habitat where breeder density has been reduced by an acorn crop failure. Also as shown in Figure 41, there is movement of breeders from one territory to another, often from lower to higher quality habitat. Not illustrated are the relatively rare regional acorn crop failures that may result in breeder density decline and subsequent low reproductive output over a broad area, providing increased opportunity for dispersing offspring and older floaters to gain a territory and breeding status.

These patterns of habitat quality and acorn production, the varied behaviors floaters employ to acquire breeding space and exploit resources, the behavioral interactions between territorial jays and floaters, and the ability of breeders to move and improve the quality of their territories all promote selection for early dispersal and floating in scrub-jays in central coastal California, and selection against cooperative breeding.

ACKNOWLEDGMENTS

Fanny Hastings Arnold, through her continuous generosity, and the Museum of Vertebrate Zoology, provided the exquisite Hastings Natural History Reservation where this research was done. Financial assistance was provided by the Department of Forestry and Resource Conservation (Oliver Lyman Fund), the American Museum of Natural History (Frank M. Chapman Memorial Fund), Sigma Xi, the American Academy of Sciences (O. C. Marsh Fund), and the Museum of Vertebrate Zoology (Kellogg Fund). I was also supported by University Fellowships, Graduate Minority Fellowships, and a Betty S. Davis Memorial Fellowship.

I am especially grateful to Walt Koenig and Ron Mumme for their companionship at Hastings and their ideas concerning cooperative breeding. Frank Pitelka and Dale McCullough continually sent me back to the field with new ideas and rekindled enthusiasm. Numerous field assistants worked on the study: Greg Ashcroft, Bob Beffy, Clay Clifton, Sharon Dougherty, Lenore Feinburg, and Jim Siegel, all of whom braved long hours and certain exposure to poison oak in search of scrub-jay nests.

Frank Pitelka, Walter Koenig, Ron Mumme, Glen Woolfenden, John Fitzpatrick, Peter Stacey, and Dale McCullough made numerous helpful criticisms of earlier drafts. Joseph Jehl and John Rotenberry provided long-term editorial support. Karen J. Nardi provided love and understanding and both the financial and moral support needed to complete the study. To all of these individuals I give my sincere thanks.

LITERATURE CITED

ALTMANN, J. 1974. Observational study of behavior: sampling methods. Behaviour 49:227–267.

ARCESE, P. 1987. Age, intrusion pressure, and defense against floaters by territorial male Song Sparrows. Animal Behaviour 35:773–784.

ARCESE, P., AND J. N. M. SMITH. 1985. Phenotypic correlates and ecological consequences of dominance in Song Sparrows. Journal of Animal Ecology 54:817–830.

ARNOLD, K. E., AND I. P. F. OWENS. 1998. Cooperative breeding in birds: a comparative test of the life history hypothesis. Proceedings of the Royal Society of London, Series B 265:739–745.

ARNOLD, K. E., AND I. P. F. OWENS. 1999. Cooperative breeding in birds: the role of ecology. Behavioral Ecology 10:465–471.

ATWOOD, J. L. 1978. The breeding biology of the Santa Cruz Island Scrub Jay, *Aphelocoma coerulescens insularis*. M.A. thesis. California State University, Long Beach, CA.

ATWOOD, J. L. 1980a. Social interactions in the Santa Cruz Island Scrub Jay. Condor 82:440–448.

ATWOOD, J. L. 1980b. Breeding biology of the Santa Cruz Island Scrub Jay. Pp. 675–688 *in* D. M. Power (editor). The California Islands: proceedings of a multidisciplinary symposium. Santa Barbara Museum of Natural History, Santa Barbara, CA.

ATWOOD, J. L., M. J. ALPERS, AND C. T. COLLINS. 1990. Survival of breeders in Santa Cruz and mainland California Scrub Jay populations. Condor 92:783–788.

AUSTAD, S. N., AND K. N. RABENOLD. 1985. Reproductive enhancement by helpers and an experimental inquiry into its mechanism in the Bicolored Wren. Behavioral Ecology and Sociobiology 17:19–27.

AUSTAD, S. N., AND K. N. RABENOLD. 1987. Demography and the evolution of cooperative breeding in the Bicolored Wren, *Campylorhynchus griseus*. Behaviour 97:308–324.

BAEYENS, G. 1981. Functional aspects of serial monogamy: the magpie pair-bond in relation to its territorial system. Ardea 69:145–166.

BARBER, C. A., AND R. J. ROBERTSON. 1999. Floater males engage in extrapair copulations with resident female Tree Swallows. Auk 116:264–269.

BARBOUR, M. G., AND J. MAJOR. 1977. Terrestrial vegetation of California. Wiley-Interscience, New York, NY.

BEECHER, M. D., AND I. M. BEECHER. 1979. Sociobiology of Bank Swallows: reproductive strategy of the male. Science 205:1282–1285.

BELL, H. L., AND H. A. FORD. 1986. A comparison of the social organization of three syntopic species of Australian thornbill, *Acanthiza*. Behavioral Ecology and Sociobiology 19:381–392.

BOCK, C. E., AND J. H. BOCK. 1974. Geographical ecology of the Acorn Woodpecker: diversity versus abundance of resources. American Naturalist 108:694–698.

BREININGER, D. R., V. L. LARSON, B. W. DUNCAN, R. B. SMITH, D. M. ODDY, AND M. F. GOODCHILD. 1995. Landscape patterns of Florida Scrub Jay use and demographic success. Conservation Biology 9:1442–1435.

BREININGER, D. R., V. L. LARSON, D. M. ODDY, R. B. SMITH, AND M. J. BARKASZI. 1996. Florida Scrub-Jay demography in different landscapes. Auk 113:617–625.

BROWN, J. L. 1963. Social organization and behavior of the Mexican Jay. Condor 65:126–153.

BROWN, J. L. 1969. Territorial behavior and population regulation in birds. Wilson Bulletin 81: 293–329.

BROWN, J. L. 1970. Cooperative breeding and altruistic behavior in the Mexican Jay, *Aphelocoma ultamarina*. Animal Behaviour 18:366–378.

BROWN, J. L. 1974. Alternate routes to sociality in jays – with a theory for the evolution of altruism and communal breeding. American Zoologist 14:63–80.

BROWN, J. L. 1978. Avian communal systems. Annual Review of Ecology and Systematics 9: 123–156.

BROWN, J. L. 1982. Optimal group size in animals. Journal of Theoretical Biology 95:793–810.

BROWN, J. L. 1985. The evolution of helping behavior – an ontogenetic and comparative perspective. Pp. 137–171 *in* E. Gollin (editor). The comparative development of adaptive skills: evolutionary implications. Lawrence Erlbaum Associates, Hillsdale, NJ.

BROWN, J. L. 1986. Cooperative breeding and the regulation of numbers. International Ornithological Congress 18:774–782.

BROWN, J. L. 1987. Ecology and evolution of helping and communal breeding in birds. Princeton University Press, Princeton, NJ.

BROWN, J. L. 1994. Mexican Jay (*Aphelocoma ultramarina*). *In* A. Poole and F. Gill (editors). The Birds of North America, No. 118. The Academy of Natural Sciences, Philadelphia, PA, and The American Ornithologists' Union, Washington, D.C.

BROWN, J. L., AND E. S. BROWN. 1981a. Extended family system in a communal bird. Science 211: 313–324.

BROWN, J. L., AND E. S. BROWN. 1981b. Kin selection and individual selection in babblers. Pp. 244–256 *in* R. D. Alexander and D. W. Tinkle (editors). Natural selection and social behavior: recent research and new theory. Chiron Press, New York, NY.

BROWN, J. L., AND E. S. BROWN. 1984. Parental facilitation: parent–offspring relationships in communally breeding birds. Behavioral Ecology and Sociobiology 14:203–209.

BROWN, J. L., AND E. R. BROWN. 1990. The Mexican Jay: uncooperative breeding. Pp. 267–288 *in* P. B. Stacey and and W. D. Koenig (editors). Cooperative breeding in birds: long-term studies of ecology and behavior. Cambridge University Press, New York, NY.

BROWN, J. L., E. R. BROWN, S. D. BROWN, AND D. D. DOW. 1982. Helpers: effects of experimental removal on reproductive success. Science 215:421–422.

BROWN, J. L., E. R. BROWN, J. SEDRANSK, AND S. RITTER. 1997. Dominance, age, and reproductive success in a complex society: a long-term study of the Mexican Jay. Auk 114:279–286.

BROWN, J. L., AND E. G. HORVATH. 1989. Geographic variation of group size, ontogeny, rattle calls, and body size in *Aphelocoma ultramarina*. Auk 106:124–128.

BROWN, J. L., AND S.-H. LI. 1995. Phylogeny of social behavior in *Aphelocoma* jays: a role for hybridization? Auk 112:464–472.

BURT, D. B. 1996. Habitat-use patterns in cooperative and non-cooperative breeding birds: testing predictions with Western Scrub-Jays. Wilson Bulletin 108:712–727

BURT, D. B., AND A. T. PETERSON. 1993. Biology of the cooperatively breeding Scrub Jays (*Aphelocoma coerulescens*) of Oaxaca, Mexico. Auk 110:207–214.

CAFFREY, C. 1992. Female-biased delayed dispersal and helping in American Crows. Auk 109: 609–619.

CARACO, T. 1979a. Time budgeting and group size: a test of theory. Ecology 60:618–627.

CARACO, T. 1979b. Time budgeting and group size: a theory. Ecology 60:611–617.

CARMEN, W. J., W. D. KOENIG, AND R. L. MUMME. 1987. Acorn production by five species of oaks over a seven year period at the Hastings Reservation, Carmel Valley, CA. Pp. 429–434 *in* T. R. Plumb and N. H. Pillsbury (editors). Proceedings of the symposium on multiple-use management of California hardwood resources. USDA Forest Service Technical Bulletin PSW-100. USDA Forest Service, Pacific Southwest Forest and Range Experiment Station, Albany, CA.

CARRICK, R. 1963. Ecological significance of territory in the Australian Magpie, *Gymnorhina tibicen*. International Ornithological Congress 13:740–753.

CARRICK, R. 1972. Population ecology of the Australian Black-backed Magpie, Royal Penguin, and Silver Gull. Pp. 41–99 *in* Population ecology of migratory birds: a symposium. U.S. Department of the Interior Wildlife Research Report 2. USDI, Washington, D.C.

CAUGHLEY, G. 1977. Analysis of vertebrate populations. John Wiley, New York, NY.

CHARLES, J. K. 1972. Territorial behavior and the limitation of population size in crows, *Corvus corone* and *C. cornix*. Ph.D. dissertation. University of Aberdeen, Aberdeen, Scotland.

CRAIG, J. L., AND I. G. JAMIESON. 1990. Pukeko: different approaches and some different answers. Pp. 385–412 *in* P. B. Stacey and W. D. Koenig (editors). Cooperative breeding in birds: long-term studies of ecology and behavior. Cambridge University Press, New York, NY.

CUSTER, T. W., AND F. A. PITELKA. 1977. Demographic features of a Lapland Longspur population near Barrow, Alaska. Auk 94:505–525.

DEGANGE, A. R. 1976. The daily and annual time budget of the Florida Scrub Jay. M.A. thesis. University of South Florida, Tampa, FL.

DEGANGE, A. R., J. W. FITZPATRICK, J. W. LAYNE, AND G. E. WOOLFENDEN. 1989. Acorn harvesting by Florida Scrub Jays. Ecology 70:348–356.

EDEN, S. F. 1987. Dispersal and competitive ability in the magpie: an experimental study. Animal Behaviour 35:764–772.

EDWARDS, T. C., JR. 1986. Ecological distribution of the Gray-breasted Jay: the role of habitat. Condor 88:456–460.

EDWARDS, S. V., AND S. NAEEM. 1993. The phylogenetic component of cooperative breeding in perching birds. American Naturalist 141:754–789.

EKMAN, J., AND C. ASKENMO. 1984. Social rank and habitat use in Willow Tit groups. Animal Behaviour 32:508–514.

EKMAN, J., AND C. ASKENMO. 1986. Reproductive cost, age-specific survival, and comparison of the reproductive strategy in two European tits (genus *Parus*). Evolution 40:159–168.

ELKIN, R. G., W. R. FEATHERSTON, AND J. C. ROGLER. 1978. Investigations of leg abnormalities in chicks consuming high tannin sorghum grain diets. Poultry Science 57:757–762.

EMLEN, S. T. 1982. The evolution of helping. I. An ecological constraints model. American Naturalist 119:29–39.

FITZPATRICK, J. W., AND G. E. WOOLFENDEN. 1986. Demographic routes to cooperative breeding in some New World jays. Pp. 137–160 *in* M. H. Nitecki and J. A. Kitchell (editors). Evolution of animal behavior. Oxford University Press, Oxford, UK.

FITZPATRICK, J. W., AND G. E. WOOLFENDEN. 1988. Components of lifetime reproductive success in the Florida Scrub Jay. Pp. 305–320 *in* T. H. Clutton-Brock (editor). Reproductive success. University of Chicago Press, Chicago, IL.

FITZPATRICK, J. W., G. E. WOOLFENDEN, AND K. J. MCGOWAN. 1989. Sources of variance in lifetime fitness of Florida Scrub Jays. International Ornithological Congress 19:876–91.

FREED, L. A. 1986. Territory takeover and sexually selected infanticide in tropical House Wrens. Behavioral Ecology and Sociobiology 19:197–206.

FRETWELL, S. 1969. Dominance behavior and winter habitat distribution in juncos (*Junco hymalis*). Bird-Banding 40:1–25.

GAYOU, D. C. 1986. The social system of the Texas Green Jay. Auk 103:540–547.

GIBBS, H. L., AND P. R. GRANT. 1987. Adult survivorship in Darwin's Ground Finch (*Geospiza*) populations in a variable environment. Journal of Animal Ecology 56:797–813.

GLASE, J. C. 1973. Ecology of social organization in the Black-capped Chickadee. Living Bird 12:235–267.

GOLDMAN, P. 1980. Flocking as a possible predator defense in Dark-eyed Juncos. Wilson Bulletin 92:88–95.

GOWATY, P. A. 1985. Multiple parentage and apparent monogamy in birds. Ornithological Monographs 37:11–21.

GRIMES, L. G. 1980. Observations of group behavior and breeding biology of the Yellow-billed Shrike *Corvinella corvina*. Ibis 122:166–192.

HANNON, S. J., R. L. MUMME, W. D. KOENIG, AND F. A. PITELKA. 1985. Acorn crop failure, dominance, and a decline in numbers in the cooperatively breeding Acorn Woodpecker. Journal of Animal Ecology 56:197–207.

HARVEY, P. H., P. J. GREENWOOD, C. M. PERRINS, AND A. R. MARTIN. 1979. Breeding success of Great Tits *Parus major* in relation to age of male and female parent. Ibis 121:216–219.

HATCHWELL, B. J., A. F. RUSSELL, M. K. FOWLIE, AND D. J. ROSS. 1999. Reproductive success and nest-site selection in a cooperative breeder: effect of experience and a direct benefit of helping. Auk:355–363.

HEINSOHN, R. G. 1991. Slow learning of foraging skills and extended parental care in cooperatively breeding White-winged Choughs. American Naturalist 137:864–881.

HEINSOHN, R. G., A. COCKBURN, AND R. B. CUNNINGHAM. 1988. Foraging, delayed maturation, and advantages of cooperative breeding in White-winged Choughs, *Corcorax melanorhamptos*. Ethology 77:177–186.

HEINSOHN, R. G., A. COCKBURN, AND R. A. MULDER. 1990. Avian cooperative breeding: old hypotheses and new directions. Trends in Ecology and Evolution 5:403–407.

HUNTER, L. A. 1987. Acquisition of territories by floaters in cooperatively breeding Purple Gallinules. Animal Behaviour 35:402–410.

HURLY, T. A., AND R. J. ROBERTSON. 1984. Aggression and territorial behavior in female Red-winged Blackbirds. Canadian Journal of Zoology 62:148–153.

HÖGSTEDT, G. 1980. Evolution of clutch size in birds: adaptive variation in relation to territory quality. Science 210:1148–1150.

INNES, K. E., AND R. E. JOHNSTON. 1996. Cooperative breeding in the White-throated Magpie-Jay. How do auxiliaries influence nesting success? Animal Behaviour 51:519–533.

JAMES, F. C., AND H. H. SHUGART, JR. 1970. A quantitative method of habitat description. Audubon Field Notes 24:727–736.

JAMES, P. C., AND N. A. M. VERBEEK. 1984. Temporal and energetic aspects of food storage in Northwestern Crows. Ardea 72:207–215.

KLOMP, H. 1970. The determination of clutch size in birds: a review. Ardea 58:1–124.

KOENIG, W. D. 1981. Space competition in the Acorn Woodpecker: power struggles in a cooperative breeder. Animal Behaviour 29:396–427.

KOENIG, W. D., W. J. CARMEN, R. L. MUMME, AND M. STANBACK. 1994b. Acorn production by oaks in central coastal California: variation within and among years. Ecology 75:99–109.

KOENIG, W. D., J. M. H. KNOPS, W. J. CARMEN, M. STANBACK, AND R. L. MUMME. 1994a. Estimating acorn crops using visual surveys. Canadian Journal of Forest Research 24:2105–2112.

KOENIG, W. D., AND R. L. MUMME. 1987. Population ecology of the Acorn Woodpecker. Princeton University Press, Princeton, NJ.

KOENIG, W. D., AND F. A. PITELKA. 1981. Ecological factors and kin selection in the evolution of cooperative breeding in birds. Pp. 261–280 in R. D. Alexander and D. W. Tinkle (editors). Natural selection and social behavior: recent research and new theory. Chiron Press, New York, NY.

KOENIG, W. D., F. A. PITELKA, W. J. CARMEN, R. L. MUMME, AND M. STANBACH. 1992. The evolution of delayed dispersal in cooperative breeders. Quarterly Review of Biology 67:111–150.

KOFORD, R. R., B. S. BOWEN, AND S. L. VEHRENCAMP. 1990. Groove-billed Anis: joint-nesting in a tropical cuckoo. Pp. 289–332 in P. B. Stacey and W. D. Koenig (editors). Cooperative breeding in birds: long-term studies of ecology and behavior. Cambridge University Press, New York, NY.

KOMDEUR, J. 1991. Influence of territory quality and habitat saturation on dispersal options in the Seychelles Warbler: an experimental test of the habitat saturation hypothesis for cooperative breeding. International Ornithological Congress 20:1325–1332.

KOMDEUR, J. 1996. Influence of helping and breeding experience on reproductive performance in the Seychelles Warbler: a translocation experiment. Behavioral Ecology 7:326–333.

KREBS, J. R. 1971. Territory and breeding density in the Great Tit Parus major L. Ecology 52:2–22.

LACK, D. 1966. Population studies of birds. Clarendon Press, Oxford, UK.

LANGEN, T. A. 1996a. Skill acquisition and the timing of natal dispersal in the White-throated Magpie-Jay (Calocitta formosa). Animal Behaviour 51:575–588.

LANGEN, T. A. 1996b. The mating system of the White-throated Magpie-Jay Calocitta formosa and Greenwood's hypothesis for sex-biased dispersal. Ibis 138:506–513.

LANGEN, T. A. 1996c. Social learning of a novel foraging skill by White-throated Magpie-Jays (Calocitta formosa, Corvidae): a field experiement. Ethology 102:157–166.

LANGEN, T. A. AND S. L. VEHRENCAMP. 1999. Ecological factors affecting group and territory size in White-throated Magpie-Jays. Auk 115:327–339.

LAWTON, M. F., AND R. O. LAWTON. 1986. Heterochrony, deferred breeding, and avian sociality. Current Ornithology 3:187–222.

LEIGHTON, M. 1986. Hornbill social dispersion: variations on a monogamous theme. Pp. 108–130 in D. I. Rubenstein and R. W. Wrangham (editors). Ecological aspects of social evolution. Princeton University Press, Princeton, NJ.

LIGON, J. D. 1981. Demographic patterns and communal breeding in the Green Woodhoopoe, Phoeniculus purpureus. Pp. 231–243 in R. D. Alexander and D. W. Tinkle (editors). Natural selection and social behavior: recent research and new theory. Chiron Press, New York, NY.

LIGON, J. D. 1988. Cavity roosting, philopatry, and cooperative breeding in the Green Woodhoopoe may reflect a physiological trait. Auk 105: 123–127.

LIGON, J. D., AND S. H. LIGON. 1978. Communal breeding in Green Woodhoopoes as a case for reciprocity. Nature 280:174.

LOERY, G., K. H. POLLOCK, J. D. NICHOLS, AND J. E. HINES. 1987. Age-specificity of Black-capped Chickadee survival rates: analysis of capture–recapture data. Ecology. 68:1038–1044.

MACROBERTS, M. H., AND B. R. MACROBERTS. 1976. Social organization and behavior of the Acorn Woodpecker in central coastal California. Ornithological Monographs 21:1–115.

MARQUARDT, R. R., AND A. T. WARD. 1979. Chick performance as affected by autoclave treatment of tannin-containing and tannin-free cultivars of favabeans. Canadian Journal of Animal Science 59:781–789.

MARSHALL, J. T., JR. 1957. Birds of the pine–oak woodland in southern Arizona and adjacent Mexico. Pacific Coast Avifauna 32:1–125.

MATTHYSEN, E. 1987. Territory establishment of juvenile nuthatches after fledging. Ardea 75:53–58.

MCGOWAN, K. J. 1987. Social development in young Florida Scrub Jays. Ph.D. dissertation. University of South Florida, Tampa, FL.

MCGOWAN, K. J., AND G. E. WOOLFENDEN. 1989. A sentinel system in the Florida Scrub Jay. Animal Behaviour 37:1000–1006.

MUGAAS, J. N., AND J. R. KING. 1981. Annual variation of daily energy expenditure by the Black-billed Magpie: a study of thermal and behavioral energetics. Studies in Avian Biology 5: 1–78.

MUMME, R. L. 1992. Do helpers increase reproductive success? An experimental analysis in the Florida Scrub Jay. Behavioral Ecology and Sociobiology 31:319–328.

MURRAY, B. G., JR. 1984. A demographic theory on the evolution of mating systems as exemplified by birds. Evolutionary Biology 18:71–140.

MURTON, R. K., AND N. J. WESTWOOD. 1977. Avian breeding cycles. Clarendon Press, Oxford, UK.

NOBLE, G. K. 1939. The role of dominance in the social life of birds. Auk 56:263–273.

OFCARCIK, R. P., AND E. E. BURNS. 1971. Chemical and physical properties of selected acorns. Journal of Food Science 36:576–578.

PATTERSON, I. J. 1980. Territorial behavior and the limitation of population density. Ardea 68: 53–62.

PERRINS, C. M. 1970. The timing of birds' breeding season. Ibis 112:242–255.

PERRINS, C. M. 1976. Possible effects of qualitative changes in the insect diet of avian predators. Ibis 118:580–584.

PETERSON, A. T., AND D. B. BURT. 1992. Phylogenetic history of social evolution and habitat use in the *Aphelocoma* jays. Animal Behaviour 44:859–866.

PETERSON, A. T., AND D. VARGAS. 1992. Ecological diversity in Scrub Jays (*Aphelocoma coerulescens*). Pp. 66–84 *in* T. P. Ramamoorthy, R. Bye, A. Lot and J. Fa (editors). Biological diversity of Mexico: origins and distribution. Oxford University Press, New York, NY.

PITELKA, F. A. 1945. Pterylography, molt, and age determination of American jays of the genus *Aphelocoma*. Condor 47:229–260.

PITELKA, F. A. 1951. Speciation and ecological distribution in American jays of the genus *Aphelocoma*. University of California Publications in Zoology 50:195–464.

PITELKA, F. A. 1959. Numbers, breeding schedule, and territoriality in Pectoral Sandpipers of northern Alaska. Condor 61:233–264.

PITELKA, F. A. 1986. A first in the literature on avian cooperative breeding. Ecology 67:1434–1435.

POWELL, G. V. N. 1974. Experimental analysis of the social value of flocking by starlings (*Sturnus vulgaris*) in relation to predation and foraging. Animal Behaviour 22:501–505.

POWELL, R. A. 1989. Effects of resource productivity, patchiness and predictability on mating systems and dispersal strategies. Pp. 101–123 *in* V. Standen and R. A. Foley (editors). Comparative socioecology. Clarendon Press, Oxford, UK.

PRUETT-JONES, S. G., AND M. J. LEWIS. 1990. Sex ratio and habitat limitation promote delayed dispersal in Superb Fairy-wrens. Nature 348:541–542.

PULLIAM, H. R. 1976. The principle of optimal behavior and the theory of communities. Pp. 311–332 *in* P. P. G. Bateson and P. H. Klopfer (editors). Perspectives in ethology, Vol. 2. Plenum Press, New York, NY.

RABENOLD, K. N. 1984. Cooperative enhancement of reproductive success in tropical wren societies. Ecology 65:871–885.

RABENOLD, K. N. 1985. Cooperation in breeding by nonreproductive wrens: kinship, reciprocity, and demography. Behavioral Ecology and Sociobiology 17:1–17.

ROOT, R. B. 1967. The niche exploitation pattern of the Blue-gray Gnatcatcher. Ecological Monographs 37:317–350.

ROWLEY, I. 1965. The life history of the Superb Blue Wren, *Malurus cyaneus*. Emu 64:251–297.

RUTBERG, A. T., AND S. ROHWER. 1980. Breeding strategies of male Yellow-headed Blackbirds: results of a removal experiment. Auk 97:619–622.

SABINE, W. S. 1959. The winter society of the Oregon Junco: intolerance, dominance, and the pecking order. Condor 61:110–135.

SÆTHER, B.-E. 1990. Age specific variation in reproductive performance in birds. Current Ornithology 7:251–283.

SÆTHER, T. R., AND G. E. FONSTAD 1981. A removal experiment showing unmated females in a breeding population of Chaffinches. Animal Behaviour 29:637–639.

SCHAUB, R., R. L. MUMME, AND G. E. WOOLFENDEN. 1992. Predation on the eggs and nestlings of Florida Scrub Jays. Auk 109:585–593.

SCHODDE, R. 1982. Origin, adaptation and evolution of birds in Australia. Pp. 191–224 *in* W. R. Barker and P. J. M. Greenslade (editors). Evolution of the flora and fauna of arid Australia. Peacock, Frewville, Australia.

SCHOECH, S. J. 1996. The effect of supplemental food on body condition and the timing of reproduction in a cooperative breeder, the Florida Scrub-Jay. Condor 98:234–244.

SELANDER, R. K. 1964. Speciation in wrens of the genus *Campylorhynchus*. University of California Publications in Zoology 74:1–224.

SHERMAN, P. W., AND M. L. MORTON. 1984. Demography of Belding's ground squirrel. Ecology 65: 1617–1628.

SKUTCH, A. F. 1961. Helpers among birds. Condor 63:198–226.

SMITH, C. C., AND O. J. REICHMAN. 1984. The evolution of food caching by birds and mammals. Annual Review of Ecology and Systematics 15:329–352.

SMITH, J. N. M., AND P. ARCESE. 1989. How fit are floaters? Consequences of alternative territorial behavior in a nonmigratory sparrow. American Naturalist 133:830–845.

SMITH, S. M. 1978. The underworld in a territorial sparrow: adaptive strategy for floaters. American Naturalist 112:571–582.

SMITH, S. M. 1984. Flock switching in chickadees: why be a winter floater? American Naturalist 123:81–98.

SOUTHWOOD, T. R. E. 1978. Ecological methods. 2nd ed. Chapman and Hall, London, UK.

STACEY, P. B., AND C. E. BOCK. 1978. Social plasticity in the Acorn Woodpecker. Science 202: 1298–1302.

STACEY, P. B., AND J. D. LIGON. 1987. Territory quality and dispersal options in the Acorn Woodpecker, and a challenge to the habitat-saturation model of cooperative breeding. American Naturalist 130:654–676.

STACEY, P. B., AND J. D. LIGON. 1991. The benefits of philopatry hypothesis for the evolution of cooperative breeding: variance in territory quality and group size effects. American Naturalist 137:831–846.

STALLCUP, J. A., AND G. E. WOOLFENDEN. 1978. Family status and contribution to breeding by Florida Scrub Jays. Animal Behaviour 26:1144–56.

STEARNS, S. C., AND R. E. CRANDALL. 1981. Quantitative predictions of delayed maturity. Evolution 35:455–463.

STRAHL, S. D., AND J. L. BROWN. 1987. Geographic variation in social structure and behavior of *Aphelocoma ultramarina*. Condor 89:422–424.

STRAHL, S. D., AND A. SCHMITZ. 1990. Hoatzins: cooperative breeding in a folivorous neotropical bird. Pp 131–156 *in* P. B. Stacey and W. D. Koenig (editors). Cooperative breeding in birds: long-term studies of ecology and behavior. Cambridge University Press, New York, NY.

STUTCHBURY, B. J., AND R. J. ROBERTSON. 1986. Behavioral tactics of subadult female floaters in the Tree Swallow. Behavioral Ecology and Sociobiology 20:413–419.

TRAIL, P. W., S. D. STRAHL, AND J. L. BROWN. 1981. Infanticide in relation to individual and flock histories in a communally breeding bird, the Mexican Jay (*Aphelocoma ultramarina*). American Naturalist 118:72–82.

VAN BALEN, J. H. 1980. Population fluctuations of the Great Tit and feeding conditions in winter. Ardea 68:143–164.

VAN BALEN, J. H., A. J. VAN NOORDWIJK, AND J. VISSER. 1987. Lifetime reproductive success and recruitment in two Great Tit populations. Ardea 75:1–10.

VANDER WALL, S. B. 1990. Food hoarding in animals. University of Chicago Press, Chicago, IL.

VANDER WALL, S. B., AND R. P. BALDA. 1977. Coadaptations of the Clark's Nutcracker and the pinyon pine for efficient seed harvest and dispersal. Ecological Monographs 47:89–111.

VARLEY, G. C., AND G. R. GRADWELL. 1960. Key factor analysis in population studies. Journal of Animal Ecology 29:399–401.

VELTMAN, C. J. 1989. Flock, pair and group living lifestyles without cooperative breeding by Australian Magpies, *Gymnorhina tibicen*. Ibis 131:601–608.

VERBEEK, N. A. M. 1970. The exploitation system of the Yellow-billed Magpie. Ph.D. dissertation. University of California, Berkeley, CA.

VERBEEK, N. A. M. 1973. The exploitation system of the Yellow-billed Magpie. University of California Publications in Zoology 99:1–58.

WAITE, T. A., AND D. STRICKLAND. 1997. Cooperative breeding in Gray Jays: philopatric offspring provision juvenile siblings. Condor 99:523–525.

WAINIO, W. W., AND E. B. FORBES. 1941. The chemical composition of forest fruits and nuts from Pennsylvania. Journal of Agricultural Research 62:627–635.

WALTERS, J. R. 1990. Red-cockaded Woodpeckers: a "primitive" cooperative breeder. Pp. 67–102 *in* P. B. Stacey and W. D. Koenig (editors). Cooperative breeding in birds: long-term studies of ecology and behavior. Cambridge University Press, New York, NY.

WALTERS, J. R., C. K. COPEYON, AND J. H. CARTER, III. 1992b. A test of the ecological basis of cooperative breeding in Red-cockaded Woodpeckers. Auk 109:90–97.

WALTERS, J. R., P. D. DOERR, AND J. H. CARTER, III. 1992a. Delayed dispersal and reproduction as a life-history tactic in cooperative breeders: fitness calculations from Red-cockaded Woodpeckers. American Naturalist 139:623–643.

WASER, P. M. 1981. Sociality or territorial defense: the influence of resource renewal. Behavioral Ecology and Sociobiology 8:231–237.

WASER, P. M. 1988. Resources, philopatry, and social interactions among mammals. Pp. 109–130 *in* C. Slobodchikoff (editor). The ecology of social behavior. Academic Press, New York, NY.

WATSON, A. 1985. Social class, socially-induced loss, recruitment and breeding of Red Grouse. Oecologia 67:493–498.

WATSON, A., AND R. MOSS. 1970. Dominance, spacing behavior and aggression in relation to population limitation in vertebrates. Pp. 167–218 *in* A. Watson (editor). Animal populations in relation to their food resources. Blackwell, Oxford, UK.

WEBBER, T., AND J. L. BROWN. 1994. Natural history of the Unicolor Jay in Chiapas, Mexico. Proceedings of the Western Foundation of Vertebrate Zoology 5:135–160.

WILLIAMS, P. L., AND W. D. KOENIG. 1980. Water dependence of birds in a temperate oak woodland. Auk 97:339–350.

WOLGAST, L. J., AND B. B. STOUT. 1977. Effects of age, stand density, and fertilizer application on bear oak reproduction. Journal of Wildlife Management 41:685–691.

WOOLFENDEN, G. E. 1974. Nesting and survival in a population of Florida Scrub Jays. Living Bird 12:25–49.

WOOLFENDEN, G. E. 1975. Florida Scrub Jay helpers at the nest. Auk 92:1–15.

WOOLFENDEN, G. E., AND J. W. FITZPATRICK. 1977. Dominance in the Florida Scrub Jay. Condor 79:1–12.

WOOLFENDEN, G. E., AND J. W. FITZPATRICK. 1978. The inheritance of territory in group-breeding birds. BioScience 28:104–108.

WOOLFENDEN, G. E., AND J. W. FITZPATRICK. 1984. The Florida Scrub Jay: demography of a cooperative-breeding bird. Princeton University Press, Princeton, NJ.

WOOLFENDEN, G. E., AND J. W. FITZPATRICK. 1986. Sexual asymmetries in the life history of the Florida Scrub Jay. Pp. 87–107 *in* D. I. Rubenstein and R. W. Wrangham (editors). Ecological aspects of social evolution. Princeton University Press, Princeton, NJ.

WOOLFENDEN, G. E., AND J. W. FITZPATRICK. 1990. The Florida Scrub Jay: a synopsis after 18 years of study. Pp 239–266 *in* P. B. Stacey and W. D. Koenig (editors). Cooperative breeding in birds: long-term studies of ecology and behavior. Cambridge University Press, New York, NY.

ZACK, S. 1990. Coupling delayed breeding with short-distance dispersal in cooperatively breeding birds. Ethology 86:265–286.

ZACK, S., AND J. D. LIGON. 1985a. Cooperative breeding in *Lanius* shrikes. I. Habitat and demography of two sympatric species. Auk 102:754–765.

ZACK, S., AND J. D. LIGON. 1985b. Cooperative breeding in *Lanius* shrikes. II. Maintenance of group living in a nonsaturated habitat. Auk 102:766–773.

ZACK, S., AND K. N. RABENOLD. 1989. Assessment, age and proximity in dispersal contests among cooperative wrens: field experiments. Animal Behaviour 38:235–247.